Tim Manson

CCEA GCSE

GEOGRAPHY STUDY GUIDE UNIT 1

Understanding Our Natural World

COLOURPOINT
EDUCATIONAL

© 2023 Tim Manson and Colourpoint
    Creative Ltd

ISBN: 978 1 78073 215 2

First Edition
First Impression

Layout and design: April Sky Design
Printed by: GPS Colour Graphics Ltd, Belfast

COLOURPOINT EDUCATIONAL

Colourpoint Educational
An imprint of Colourpoint Creative Ltd
Colourpoint House
Jubilee Business Park
21 Jubilee Road
Newtownards
County Down
Northern Ireland
BT23 4YH

Tel: 028 9182 0505
E-mail: sales@colourpoint.co.uk
Website: www.colourpoint.co.uk

The Author

Tim Manson learned to love Geography from an early age. He is a graduate of Queens' University, Belfast, the University of Ulster and the Open University. He has been teaching Geography for over 27 years and is the Vice Principal at Cullybackey College. He is a Principal Examiner for an awarding body in Geography and is a keen advocate for creative uses of ICT in learning and teaching. He has a highly successful website: www.thinkgeography.net

Acknowledgements

Thanks to Colourpoint for giving me the opportunity to realise a dream. Big thanks to my editor Rachel Allen, who kept me on my toes throughout, and to Wesley Johnston for the great diagrams. Thanks to my colleagues at Cullybackey College who have welcomed me into the Geography fold. Thanks to my students both present and past – little did you know that you were helping to refine my ideas and material. Finally, to my wife, Helen, and to Erin and Isaac, thanks for putting up with me while I spent so much time tapping on my key board, and for helping make all the 'field trips' special!

Contents

How to use this book

This study guide is divided into two sections:

1. Study material

This addresses the key features of the CCEA GCSE Geography specification, the case studies and the key geographical terms. It also offers revision tips.

 Key geographical terms

These key geographical terms are used throughout the specification. Each term is clearly defined.

 Test your revision

These questions are designed to check your understanding of the course content. You can get someone to ask you the questions or test yourself.

 Revision tip

These tips offer examiner guidance on what areas to focus on, how to avoid confusion and what might be asked on the exam.

2. Practice questions

This includes exam-style questions, tips on how to answer them and sample answers. It also offers examiner advice on how to get the best grade possible, develop your exam technique and improve your revision skills.

Study Material

Theme A	**River environments**
	1. The drainage basin: a component of the water cycle
	2. River processes and landforms
	3. Sustainable management of rivers

Part 1	**The drainage basin: a component of the water cycle**

 Key geographical terms

Drainage basin: The area of land that is drained by a river and its tributaries.

Water cycle: A natural system where water is in constant movement above, on or below the surface of the Earth, and is changing state from water vapour (gas) to liquid and to ice (solid).

Interception: When water is trapped by vegetation (store) before it reaches the ground.

Watershed: The dividing line between one drainage basin and another.

Source: The starting point of a river.

Tributary: A small river or stream that flows into a larger river.

Confluence: Where two rivers meet.

River mouth: The place where the river flows into the sea.

The water cycle

The **water cycle** is a natural system where water is in constant movement above, on or below the surface of the Earth, and is changing state from water vapour (gas) to liquid and to ice (solid).

The water cycle

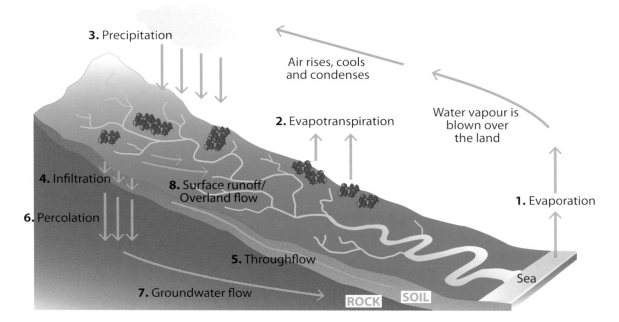

1. **Evaporation**
   Water is transformed into water vapour in the atmosphere.

2. **Evapotranspiration**
   Water is transferred from land and water surfaces to the atmosphere by evaporation and plant transpiration.

3. **Precipitation**
   Water vapour condenses into drizzle, rain, sleet, snow and hail, and this falls towards the surface of the land.

4. **Infiltration**
   Water soaks (filters) into the soil.

5. **Throughflow**
   Water moves downhill through the soil.

6. **Percolation**
   Water moves from the soil into the spaces (pores) in the rock.

7. **Groundwater flow**
   Water moves slowly through the rock back into the sea.

8. **Surface runoff/overland flow**
   Water moves across the surface of the land.

The drainage basin system

A **drainage basin** is the area of land that is drained by a river and its tributaries. When water falls onto the land the force of gravity pulls it downhill towards the sea.

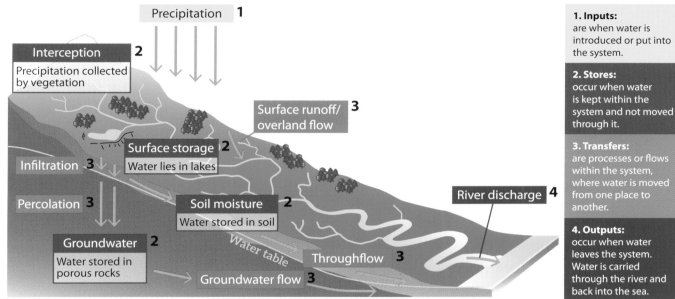

The drainage basin system

Characteristics of the drainage basin

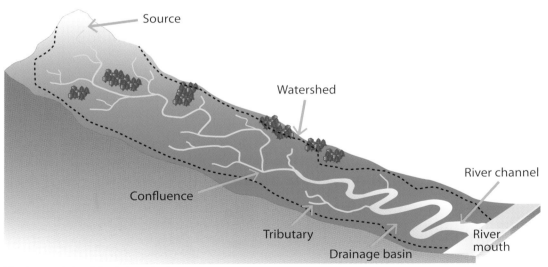

The characteristics of the drainage basin

 Revision tip

It is important that you learn the key geographical terms and understand the key elements of the water cycle and drainage basin system. These topics often feature in the exam.

How does a river change along a long profile?

The long profile is the shape of a river as it flows downstream from the source to the river mouth. Rivers can be divided up into three distinct stages (courses), each with different influences that shape the landscape through which the river flows. As the river moves downstream from the upper course, through the middle course to the lower course, the river characteristics will change.

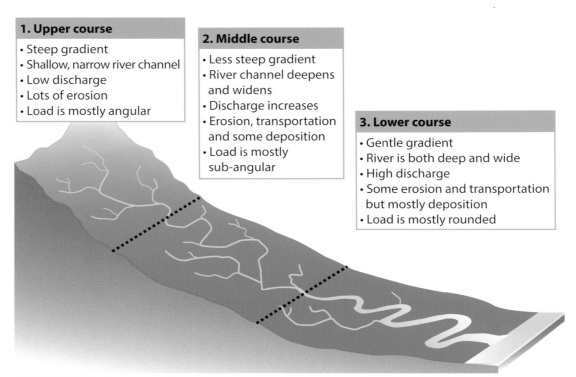

1. Upper course
- Steep gradient
- Shallow, narrow river channel
- Low discharge
- Lots of erosion
- Load is mostly angular

2. Middle course
- Less steep gradient
- River channel deepens and widens
- Discharge increases
- Erosion, transportation and some deposition
- Load is mostly sub-angular

3. Lower course
- Gentle gradient
- River is both deep and wide
- High discharge
- Some erosion and transportation but mostly deposition
- Load is mostly rounded

River characteristics along a long profile

There are five main characteristics that change as the river moves along a long profile:

1. The gradient decreases downstream
The gradient is the angle of the river bed. It decreases as the river flows from the source through the different courses (upper, middle and lower) towards the mouth. The upper course is steep but the lower course will be relatively flat.

2. The depth increases downstream
The depth is how deep the water in the river is. River depth will increase from its source to its mouth and is usually measured in centimetres.

3. The width increases downstream
The width is the distance from one riverbank to the other riverbank. River width will also increase from its source to its mouth and is usually measured in metres.

4. The discharge increases downstream

The discharge is the amount of water that passes a point in a river at a particular time. It is measured in cumecs – cubic metres of water per second.

Cross-sectional area (depth and width) m^2	×	Velocity (speed) m/sec	=	Discharge m^3/sec

5. The load becomes smaller and rounder downstream

The load (also known as bedload) is the material that the river is carrying. It is mostly material that has been eroded from the riverbed and the riverbanks.

The size and shape of bedload changes dramatically along the course of a river. The size of load can range from tiny pieces of sediment to large boulders. The greater the velocity (and discharge) of a particular river, the more load that can be carried. The stones are angular in the upper course but the sharp edges become worn down as they journey towards the lower course.

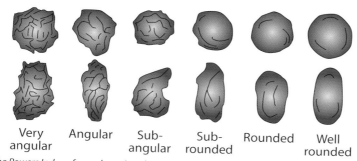

Very angular   Angular   Sub-angular   Sub-rounded   Rounded   Well rounded

The Powers Index of roundness (used to observe stone shape, angularity and roundness)

It is the erosion, transportation and deposition processes that change the shape and characteristics of the river. These are explained on the next page.

★ Test your revision

1. Describe the role of evapotranspiration in the water cycle.
2. Explain the difference between infiltration and percolation.
3. What is the difference between stores and transfers in the drainage basin system?
4. Describe three ways that a river might change along its long profile.
5. Why does the gradient of a river change as it moves downstream?
6. How would you calculate the discharge of a river?
7. Draw a diagram of a drainage basin and mark up the following features: the source, a confluence, the watershed and a tributary.

Part 2 — River processes and landforms

River processes

1. Erosion

Erosion occurs in a river when the riverbed and riverbank are worn away. The four types of erosion in a river are:

a) *Attrition:* Stones carried downstream knock against each other and start to wear each other down. This makes the load smaller and more rounded downstream.

b) *Hydraulic action:* The speed and force of the water removes material from the riverbed and banks.

c) *Abrasion/corrasion:* The force of moving water grinds the stones being carried by the river against the riverbed and banks, and this dislodges material.

d) *Solution/corrosion:* Weak acid (chemicals) in the water reacts with the rock and dissolves soluble minerals.

2. Transportation

Transportation is when the eroded material is carried from one place to another through the river system. The four types of transportation in the river are:

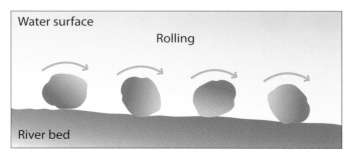

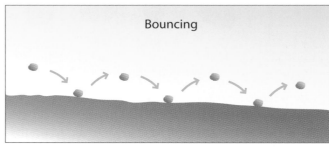

a) *Traction:* The heaviest particles of eroded material are **rolled** along the riverbed.

b) *Saltation:* Some of the heavier particles are **bounced** along the riverbed but are not held up in the flow of the river.

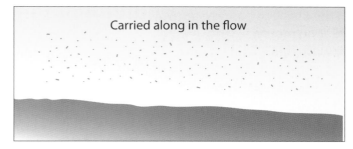

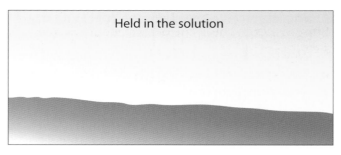

c) *Suspension:* As the water speed increases, the river picks up particles. When particles are **carried along in the flow** of the water they do not make contact with the riverbed.

d) *Solution:* Some minerals dissolve easily in the water and microscopic particles are **held up in the solution of the water.**

Revision tip

It is easy to get confused between the different erosion and transportation processes, so make sure that you learn them carefully. If might help to write the letter E (for erosion) or T (for transportation) beside each process.

3. Deposition

Deposition occurs when the river load becomes too heavy for the river to carry and material is dumped (or deposited) along the course of the river.

 Revision tip

A common exam question shows some bedload data gathered during fieldwork and asks you to describe and explain the processes that have been working on the river. You will need to be aware of the river changes downstream (see page 8) and the different ways that erosion, transportation and deposition work on the river.

 Test your revision

1. Describe the difference between erosion and transportation.
2. Explain how abrasion helps to erode the riverbanks.
3. Describe the conditions that cause traction to take place in a river.

The formation of river landforms

 Key geographical terms

River landforms: The main features that can be found along the course of a river. They are usually formed by either erosion or deposition in the river.

Waterfall: A vertical cliff of water where the water flows over a layer of hard rock on top of a layer of softer rock. The softer rock underneath is eroded away causing the cliff edge to gradually move backwards.

Meander: A bend in a river. The river flows fastest on the outside of the bend, causing erosion. The river flows slower on the inside of the bend, causing deposition.

Slip-off slope: The inside of a meander, where river load is deposited because of the slower flow of water.

River cliff: The outside of a meander, where the fast-flowing water causes erosion of the riverbank, creating a steep bank.

Floodplain: The area of land next to a river that is likely to flood. Silt is deposited when floodwater covers the area.

Levee: A build-up of material on the banks of a river caused by repeated flooding. It raises the height of the riverbank. The largest, coarsest material will be dumped close to the riverbank.

Waterfalls

Waterfalls form where water flows from an area of hard rock to an area of softer rock. Hydraulic action, abrasion and attrition all erode the softer rock, which is transported and deposited further downstream. Often the edge of the waterfall recedes, creating a gorge.

The formation of a waterfall

Hard igneous rock (basalt)

The river increases in speed here because there is no friction

Soft sedimentary rock (limestone)

Erosion

Soft rock is easily eroded to create an overhang

Force of water (hydraulic action) erodes a plunge pool

Overhang extends to reveal a ledge of hard rock

Hard rock becomes too heavy for the soft rock and cracks begin to form

Hard rock breaks off and the waterfall recedes (moves backwards)

Eroded material is transported through the river system

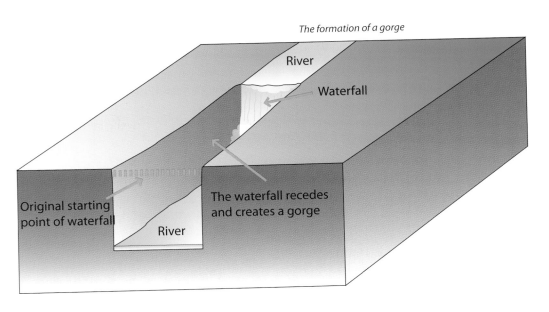

The formation of a gorge

River

Waterfall

Original starting point of waterfall

River

The waterfall recedes and creates a gorge

Meanders

Meanders occur as water moves downstream and the increased speed (velocity) of the water allows erosion to take place.

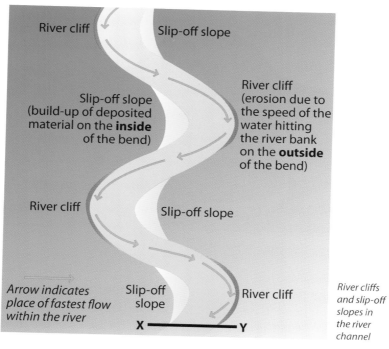

River cliff

Slip-off slope

Slip-off slope (build-up of deposited material on the **inside** of the bend)

River cliff (erosion due to the speed of the water hitting the river bank on the **outside** of the bend)

River cliff

Slip-off slope

Arrow indicates place of fastest flow within the river

Slip-off slope

River cliff

River cliffs and slip-off slopes in the river channel

Cross section through a meander

The slowest flow is on the inside of the river bend, where the river does not have enough energy to transport the eroded material and deposition begins to take place.

The fastest water flow is on the outside of the river bend, causing more erosion.

X

Y

Slip-off slope: sand and shingle deposited

Riverbed deepened by abrasion/hydraulic action

The outside bank is eroded, creating a river cliff

Small river cliff: bank will collapse

Floodplains

Floodplains are the areas of land next to a river that are likely to flood. Silt (also known as alluvium) is deposited when floodwater covers the area.

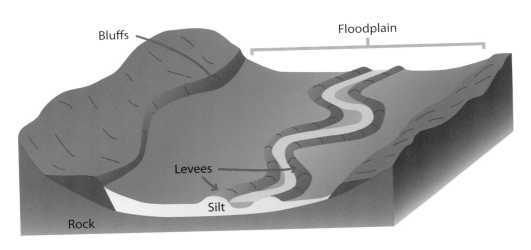

Levees

As a river floods, it deposits material across the valley floor. The largest, coarsest material is deposited first, close to the riverbank. Over time, repeated flooding of the river causes a build-up of material (silt) on the banks of the river. This is called a levee.

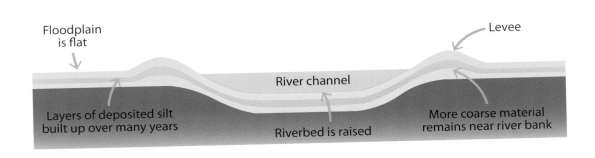

 Test your revision

1. Describe how a waterfall is formed.
2. Explain the role of two different types of erosion in the formation of a waterfall.
3. What is a meander and how is it formed?
4. What is a river cliff and how is it formed?
5. Draw a labelled diagram to show how a levee is formed.

 Revision tip

Exam questions often test your knowledge of how each river landform is formed. They are looking for detail, so make sure you that you can explain the different erosion, transportation or deposition processes that work to create each landform.

Basic map skills revision

 Revision tip

Basic map skills

Relating to Ordnance Survey (OS) maps, the CCEA GCSE Geography specification states that students should be able to:

- read maps and use the following:
  - letter and number co-ordinates.
  - four-figure and six-figure grid references.
  - the eight points of the compass.
- identify features on a plan or map by using symbols and a key.
- demonstrate knowledge and understanding of scale by measuring area, straight line distances and curved line distances.
- demonstrate knowledge and understanding of how relief is represented on OS maps (1:50,000).
- identify major relief features.
- relate cross-sectional drawings to relief features.
- analyse the interrelationship between physical and human factors on maps.

(Source: © CCEA 2022: Reproduced with permission of the Northern Ireland Council for the Curriculum, Examinations and Assessment.)

Scale and distances

Scale takes real life things and reduces them in size many times so that they can be shown on a map. The Ordnance Survey (OS) maps used in the exams will be at a scale of 1:50,000. This means that 1 cm represents 50,000 cm (500 m / half a kilometre) or 2 cm = 1 km.

- ***Measuring a straight line distance***
  The easiest way to work out distance is to use a ruler to measure from one point to another on the map and then use the scale to work out the distance in kilometres. In the example opposite, the distance has been measured as 6 cm, which is equivalent to 3 km of real distance.

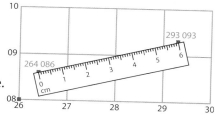

- ***Measuring a route (non-straight line) distance***
  In an exam, the best way to measure a route or non-straight line distance is to use the edge of a piece of scrap paper.

  1. Place the corner and straight edge on your starting point.
  2. Pivot the paper until the edge follows the route you want to take.
  3. Every time the route changes direction, make a small mark on the edge of the paper and pivot it so that the paper follows the route again.
  4. Repeat this process until you complete your route.
  5. Measure the distance from your first mark to your last mark on the paper. Then use the scale to work out the distance in kilometres.

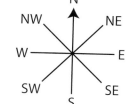

Eight points of the compass

There are eight points on the compass. You can use these to state the direction of one feature or place from another.

Grid references

OS maps are covered in a series of blue grid lines. These grid lines help you to pinpoint an exact location on the map through the use of a unique number called a grid reference.

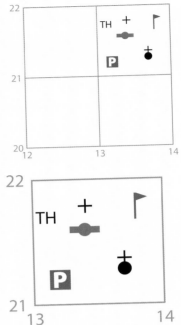

- **Four-figure grid references**
  A four-figure grid reference will help you to identify the location of a square on the map. Read the number along the bottom or top ('along the corridor'), followed by the number up the side ('up the stairs'). In the example opposite, all of the symbols are found in square 1321.

- **Six-figure grid references**
  A six-figure grid reference will help you to identify the precise location of a point *within* a square on the map. The first two numbers ('along the corridor') and the fourth and fifth numbers ('up the stairs') indicate the square that the point is found within. The third and sixth numbers are gained by drawing an imaginary grid on top of the square and assigning a number from 0 to 9 across the square.

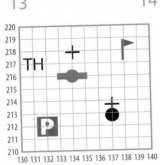

  In the example opposite, all of the symbols have a four-figure grid reference of 1321 but only one symbol has the precise location of 132212. Which one? It might help to actually draw the grid (until you get the hang of it) but you will not have time to do this during an exam, so you have to practise this skill. What are the precise six-figure grid references for the other symbols in this square?

Using symbols

Symbols are used on maps to represent important features, so that the map does not become too cluttered. The good news is that any map you get in an exam will have a key attached, so you do not need to learn the symbols. However, it is a good idea when revising river and coastal environments to look specifically at the water features and tourist information, as these are the main things that you will have to look for.

Water features

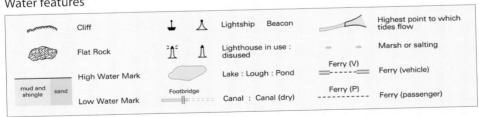

Tourist information

This is based upon Crown Copyright and is reproduced with the permission of Land & Property Services under delegated authority from the Controller of Her Majesty's Stationery Office, Crown copyright and database right 2015 PMLPA No 100496

Relief on maps

Relief is the shape and height of the land. There are three different ways that heights can be shown on an OS map:

- **Spot heights:** A black dot with the height of the land written (in metres) beside it.

- **Contour lines:** A brown line that joins places with the same height above sea level. On 1:50,000 maps, the contour line will go up every 10 m. The closer together the contour lines are, the steeper the land will be. The further away the lines are, the gentler the slopes will be.

- **Colour-shaded areas:** Some maps also use different colours within the contours to indicate the height of an area. The darker the colour, the higher up it is.

Part 3 — Sustainable management of rivers

The causes of flooding (physical and human)

 Key geographical terms

Flooding: A temporary covering by water of land that is usually dry.

Heavy rainfall or snowmelt can cause the amount of water in the river channel to overflow, leading to flooding of the surrounding floodplains that are usually dry. Rivers flood due to a combination of various physical and human factors.

Physical causes

Precipitation: The more water that falls onto a drainage basin over a short period of time, the quicker the soil becomes saturated, resulting in surface runoff.

Land use/vegetation: Vegetation intercepts and slows the passage of water into the river system.

Steepness of drainage basin: If rain falls on steep slopes, water will be drained quickly and can lead to a flash flood.

Soil and underlying rock: Sandy soils allow rainwater to infiltrate quickly, whereas clay soils stop water passing through and can increase surface run-off at a faster rate. Some rocks are permeable and allow water to pass through (e.g. limestone) whereas other rocks are impermeable (non-porous) and water will not be able to pass through them (e.g. slate).

Human causes

Deforestation: If trees are removed, this will increase the amount of surface run-off into the river channel and the risk of flooding.

Urban growth: Urban areas generally have good drainage systems that move any excess water into the river channel quickly.

River management: Narrowing the river channel or building a bridge in an inappropriate position can reduce the river capacity (amount of water it can store).

Climate change: Increased melting of ice stores (e.g. glaciers) and increased rainfall) due to processes associated with global warming could lead to more water than usual in the drainage basin systems.

Case Study: Causes of the Boscastle flood, 2004 (a case study from the British Isles)

Date:	16 August 2004
Location:	Boscastle (Cornwall, England)
Rivers involved:	Valency, Paradise and Jordan

Causes of the flooding

Physical factors

Prolonged rainfall	• It rained 12 out of 14 days in August.
Heavy rainfall	• A large depression (low pressure) produced thunderstorms. • On 16 August, 200 mm of rainfall was recorded over 24 hours. • Most of the rain fell in a five-hour period.
Steep valley sides	• The valley sides are very steep throughout the area. • The river falls 300 m in 6 km. • The water flows very quickly through the river system.

Human factors

Deforestation	• This meant there was little interception and water moved into the river channel quickly.
Urbanisation	• The old Victorian sewage system could not cope with the excess water.
The bridge factor	• Some of the bridges over the River Valency and River Jordan were old, with small arches that quickly got blocked with flood debris and fallen trees. The blockage acted like a dam and caused a surge of water when it was released.

 Revision tip

It is important that you learn some key facts and figures to support your case study answers. For this study, you should know at least two physical and two human causes of flooding in detail.

Impacts of flooding

Impact on people

1. Loss of life

- Floods can kill people. The Lynmouth flood in 1953 killed 53 people. In China, in 1931, floods are estimated to have killed over 3.7 million people.

2. Property and insurance cover

Floods can:

- damage property (e.g. water damage). The 1931 Chinese floods caused 50 million people to lose their homes due to flood damage.
- damage crops, cause animals to drown and livelihoods to be lost.
- cause public health issues (e.g. water mixing with sewage can lead to problems with drinking water and increase waterborne diseases).
- increase the cost of property insurance or make it impossible to insure property in areas at risk.
- affect poorer people in LEDCs most. Property damage can be harder to recover from as many people do not have insurance to help them rebuild.

Impact on the environment

1. Pollution

Floods can:

- wash chemicals, waste and sewage into rivers, causing pollution and killing wildlife and vegetation.

2. Destruction of wildlife habitats

Floods can:

- damage wildlife habitat. Worms, beetles, bees and caterpillar numbers can drop due to increased amounts of flooding.
- cause animals to drown.
- impact the food chain in an area.

Positive impacts

Floods can:

- bring excess water, which will replenish drinking water supplies and help with irrigation (e.g. the River Nile).
- bring alluvium (silt) to floodplains, fertilising the land and even allowing crops to grow in desert areas.
- allow fish to breed in the flood water and also swim upstream to their breeding grounds.

Test your revision

1. Describe two causes of flooding in your case study for a river in the British Isles.
2. Explain the impact that flooding can have on people and the environment.

River management methods

 Key geographical terms

Dam: A wall built across a river channel to stop the river from moving downstream, controlling the amount of water that can travel through the river system.

Levee (artificial): A man-made ridge built from rocks and sand alongside a riverbank to protect the floodplain from flooding.

Flood wall: A wall built alongside a river to prevent water from reaching the floodplain.

Embankment: An artificial bank of material (earth or rock) that can raise/strengthen the sides of a river.

Washlands: An area of land that acts as a storage area for river water to 'wash' into during a flood. It is usually found in the lower course of a river.

Land use zoning: A planning measure where land within a floodplain is divided up into areas that experience different degrees of flood risk.

Afforestation: When trees are planted to intercept rainfall and help to lower the discharge in the river.

Hard engineering methods

Hard engineering methods require major changes to the river (e.g. building new walls) to try and prevent it from flooding. These measures are not sustainable in the long term.

Dams/reservoirs	+ A dam controls the risk of flooding downstream. + Dams and reservoirs can produce hydroelectric power, which is a cheap and renewable method of energy production. + Man-made lakes and reservoirs can be used for recreation. − Both dams and reservoirs are extremely expensive. − Both have a major impact on the natural environment, changing the ecosystem completely.
Levees, embankments and flood walls	+ Levees, embankments and flood walls can be built along the riverbanks to allow the level of the river to rise without flooding the surrounding floodplain. − These can be expensive. − If water does break through an embankment or flood wall, it can be more destructive because the water will travel faster. It can also prevent the floodwater draining back into the river when the river level falls. − The natural process of silting on the floodplain will be prevented by levees, embankments and flood walls.

Channel enlargement (straightening and deepening)	+ Increasing the size of the river channel allows it to carry more water. + Water is moved more efficiently during flood events. + Rivers that meander are sometimes straightened to help increase the velocity. + Property developers prefer straight riverbanks for building housing estates and farmers prefer regular field shapes for machinery access. − The channel needs regular work as silt can build up on the riverbed. − The heavy machinery needed can be expensive and can harm delicate ecosystems. − Sometimes rivers will try to revert to their original channel. − Fish like to lay their eggs in the shallow parts of river bends. Channel deepening removes these.

Soft engineering methods

Soft engineering methods require limited changes to manage the river (e.g. afforestation) rather than prevent the river from flooding. This type of management does not damage the river and is usually more sustainable than hard engineering methods.

Washlands	+ Land can be farmed and only used in flood emergencies. + Washlands help increase friction and slow the river down. − It can be difficult to find land available close to cities.

Land use zoning	+ Land within a floodplain is divided up into areas that experience different degrees of flood risk:
	  • Red zone = places with a high chance of flooding (e.g non-residential land, parks, farmland).
	  • Amber zone = flooding is possible but unlikely (e.g. car parks, sports facilities).
	  • Green zone = flooding very unlikely (e.g residential housing).
	
	− Does not prevent flooding.

Afforestation	+ Planting trees in the upper course of a drainage basin will help reduce floods, as trees intercept and store water. − It takes a long time for the trees to grow large enough to intercept and store a lot of water. −/+ Afforestation does not prevent flooding but can help reduce its likelihood.

Sustainability

In the exam you may be asked to consider the sustainability of these different engineering measures.

1. **Social sustainability:** Will the strategy improve people's quality of life?

2. **Economic sustainability:** Is the strategy expensive to build and maintain or is it just a one-off cost? Will the strategy last for a long time?

3. **Environmental sustainability:** Is the strategy good or damaging to the environment? Does it help protect wildlife and animal habitats?

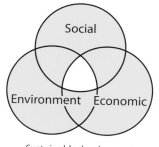

Sustainable development

 Test your revision

1. What is the difference between hard and soft engineering methods?
2. Name and describe three hard engineering methods.
3. Name and describe three soft engineering methods.

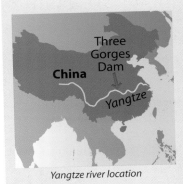

Yangtze river location

Case Study: The Yangtze river, China
(a case study from outside the British Isles)

| Location: | Yangtze (Changjiang) river, China |

The need for a river management strategy

Due to the population explosion in China from the 1950s onwards, the amount of human activity around the Yangtze river has increased the impacts of any flood event.

River management methods

Method	Description	Advantages	Disadvantages
1. Three Gorges Dam Project (TGP)	• The TGP controls a drainage area of 1 million km². • The TGP built a dam across the Yangtze. Work started in 1994 and cost £30 billion. • The dam flooded 140 towns and forced the evacuation of 1.2 million people. • The lake behind the dam wall has a maximum height of 185 m and an area of over 1000 km². • The TGP provides storage for 22.15 billion m³ of water.	• The dam is designed to protect 100 million people downstream. • The dam regulates the amount of water in the river. • The dam produces 'green' HEP energy.	• Most floods in recent years happen below the TGP. • There are often earthquakes and landslides in the area. • Much of the land used for resettlement has poor soils and is unsuitable for farming. • With people now more concentrated in urban living, this has increased the amount of pollution and sewage in the area. • The dam has devastated local ecosystems. • The river dolphin (Baiji) are close to extinction.
2. Levees	• Over 3600 km of levees have been built along the river channel.	• These levees have been built to protect 80 million people. • They are designed to handle a 10- to 30-year frequency flood.	• In 1998, the Yangtze flooded over the top of the levees, killing 3000 people and leaving 30 million homeless.
3. Washlands/ detention basins	• These are low-lying areas/ lakes that are set aside for temporary flood storage. • There are 40 major basins, which can store 50 billion m³ of water.	• They are easier to construct than dams. • Land can be used for other purposes such as farming.	• The Dongting lake has become silted up, which can increase the flooding risk. • The area in unsafe during flooding. There is no flood proofing for buildings or main roads to ensure swift evacuation. • In 1998, 300,000 people had to be moved to safety.

4. Flood warning systems	• Sensors placed in the upper course of the river are designed to give warning of increased/dangerous water levels.	• These are designed to give people time to move out of an area. • 180 monitoring stations have been built on the Yangtze.	• The system cost over £9 million.

How sustainable are these projects?

The government claims that these methods of river management are sustainable. In particular, the dam:

+ saves lives.
+ produces clean electricity.
+ allows safe shipping through the river systems.
+ means that there is a consistent water supply during droughts.

Others argue that all of the management strategies are not sustainable as:

− they damage the environment (cause landslides and the river dolphin is close to extinction).
− they cost far too much.
− they flooded the homes of millions of people and caused their relocation.
− they risk catastrophe if the dam wall bursts.
− the dam will silt up over time.

 Test your revision

Evaluate the river management strategy used on a river outside of the British Isles that you have studied.

 Revision tip

• The command word 'Evaluate' is often used in questions that require specific case study knowledge.
• Remember that an evaluation should look at both the advantages and disadvantages of a strategy.
• In this study, you need to discuss the good and bad points of two different management methods.
• It might be easier to look at one hard and one soft method or one more sustainable and one less sustainable method.
• Examiners will be looking for detail in any answer and a concluding statement evaluating how sustainable the management strategy is.

Theme B

Coastal Environments

1. Coastal processes and landforms
2. Sustainable management of coasts

Part 1 — Coastal processes and landforms

Constructive and destructive waves

Waves are created by the transfer of energy as the wind blows across the surface of the sea. The size of any wave depends on its **fetch**. The fetch is the distance that a wave travels in open water. The longer the fetch, the larger the potential wave is likely to be.

Fetch of waves

As waves begin to approach the shore, the water that rushes up the beach is called **swash** and the return flow is called **backwash**.

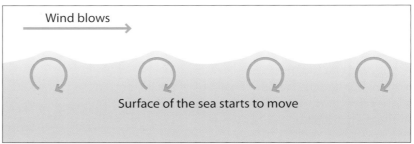

Wind blows

Surface of the sea starts to move

How waves are created

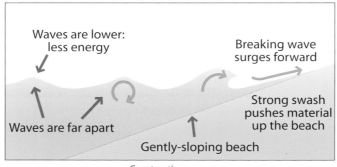

Waves are lower: less energy

Breaking wave surges forward

Waves are far apart

Strong swash pushes material up the beach

Gently-sloping beach

Constructive waves

Constructive waves

These are waves that surge up the beach. They help to build up a beach. They are gentle, flat and shallow (around 1 m high), and their energy is limited. The waves break at a rate of only a few waves per minute (between six and nine).

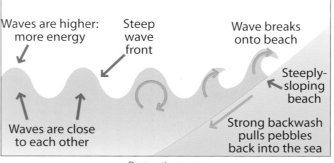

Waves are higher: more energy

Steep wave front

Wave breaks onto beach

Waves are close to each other

Steeply-sloping beach

Strong backwash pulls pebbles back into the sea

Destructive waves

Destructive waves

These are waves that break onto a steeply-sloping beach. They help to erode a beach. They are steep (5–6 m high) and close together, and have a lot of energy. The waves break more often than constructive waves, at a rate of around 15 per minute.

The table below shows some of the differences between constructive and destructive waves.

Constructive waves	Destructive waves
Strong swash and weak backwash	Weak swash and strong backwash
Usually occur in calm weather	Usually occur in storm conditions
Breaks less frequently (between 6 and 9 per minute)	Breaks frequently (around 15 per minute)
Gently-sloping beaches (stronger swash adds material to the beach)	Steeply-sloping beach (strong backwash pulls material into the sea)
Shallow waves (about 1 m high)	Steep waves (5–6 m high)
Build-up of sediment on beach	Removes sediment from the beach
Low energy	High energy
Deposit beach material	Erode the beach

Coastal processes

1. Erosion

a) *Abrasion/corrasion:* The force of moving water grinds the stones being carried by the sea against the cliffs and rocks (acting like sandpaper). This dislodges material.

b) *Attrition:* Stones and boulders that are being carried by the sea knock together and start to wear each other down. This knocks the edges off the stones and results in smaller and rounder stones.

c) *Solution/corrosion:* Salts and acids in the seawater slowly dissolve coastal cliffs.

d) *Hydraulic action:* The force of the water pounds against the cliffs and dislodges more material.

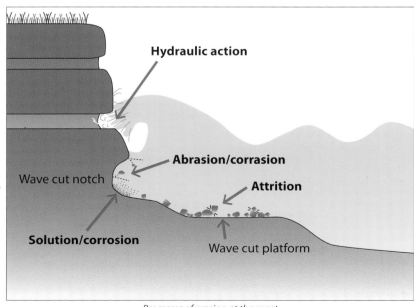

Processes of erosion at the coast

2. Transportation

Material in the sea is transported using the same four methods as rivers (traction, saltation, suspension and solution) but most material is carried along the coast by a process called **longshore drift**.

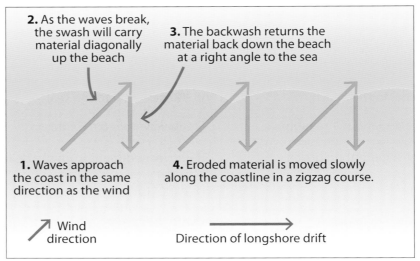

2. As the waves break, the swash will carry material diagonally up the beach

3. The backwash returns the material back down the beach at a right angle to the sea

1. Waves approach the coast in the same direction as the wind

4. Eroded material is moved slowly along the coastline in a zigzag course.

Wind direction

Direction of longshore drift

Longshore drift transporting material along the coast

3. Deposition

When waves lose energy, they dump (deposit) the material they were carrying. This can form a beach and other landforms (see pages 28–29).

The formation of coastal landforms

Erosional landforms

Headlands: These are formed when outcrops of harder, resistant rock and softer, less resistant rock are found in the same areas. Waves gradually erode the softer rock away, leaving a headland.

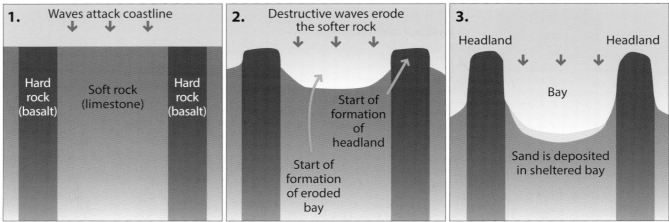

1. Waves attack coastline

Hard rock (basalt) | Soft rock (limestone) | Hard rock (basalt)

2. Destructive waves erode the softer rock

Start of formation of headland

Start of formation of eroded bay

3. Headland Headland

Bay

Sand is deposited in sheltered bay

Aerial view of the formation of a headland

Key geographical terms

Cliff: A high, steep rock face that is caused by coastal erosion.

Wave cut notches: These are formed when waves start to undercut the foot of a cliff. The notch continues to widen and undermines the headland's foundation, which causes the cliff to collapse and retreat backwards.

Wave cut platforms: These are left behind as cliffs continue to retreat from their original position. They are gently-sloping flat platforms that can be seen at low tide.

Erosion processes will continue to attack the rocks on the coast.

Wave cut notches and platforms

- Over time, **cracks** will appear in the cliff rocks. Abrasion and the continuous impact of the water (hydraulic action) will widen any weaknesses or cracks in the rock into **caves**.
- Further erosion causes the cave to erode through the headland until it forms an **arch**.
- Erosion causes the top of the arch to be undermined until eventually the weight of the rock becomes too heavy and the roof of the arch collapses.
- This leaves a **stack**, which will also be attacked by the waves. This will eventually be undercut and worn away to leave a **stump**.

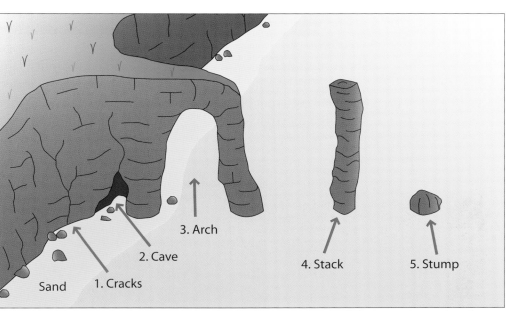

Cliffs, caves, arches, stacks and stumps

Depositional landforms

Beaches: These are gently-sloping areas of land that are found between the high and low water tide marks. They are built up by constructive waves moving deposited material (sand, shingle and pebbles) up the beach. They are generally fully covered by water at high tide and can be fully exposed at low tide.

Most beaches are made up with either sand-sized material (up to 2 mm) or pebbles and shingle (4–64 mm). Generally the larger the beach material, the steeper the slope of the beach.

Sandy beaches: These beaches are made up of very small material (up to 2 mm). Surging waves move coarser material (larger grains of sand) up the beach, while finer material (smaller grains of sand) remains close to the water. Usually sandy beaches will have a gently-sloping profile – up to 5 degrees.

Larger grains of sand are gradually moved up the beach and form a sand dune

Gently-sloping beach profile

Shingle beaches: These beaches are made up of much larger material (from 4 mm to 64 mm). The beaches may contain ridges in the profile, as during stormy conditions the waves throw larger pieces of shingle high up the beach. When the water level drops, this deposited material remains. Usually shingle beaches will be steep – over 10 degrees.

Steep beach profile is built up by larger pieces of shingle material

Large boulder material remains at the base of the beach while shingle material is 'thrown' further up the beach

The formation of a spit

A spit is a long, narrow ridge of land that is made up from deposited material (sand and shingle) along a coastline. There are a number of conditions needed before a hooked spit can form:

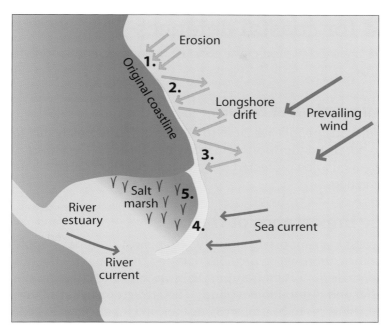

- They are found in areas where the material forming the coastline is easily eroded. **(1)**
- They are formed when prevailing winds help to transport material down the coast by longshore drift. **(2 and 3)**
- They occur where the coastline changes direction (usually where a river estuary meets the sea).
- The energy from the sea and the river meet at one place and this is where deposition takes place. The process of longshore drift continues, sand is deposited and builds up to form a spit. **(4)**
- Often the area behind the spit will become a salt marsh. **(5)**
- As the spit grows out into the deeper water of an estuary or a bay, the tip of the spit may be shaped by wave action to form a hooked spit.

 Test your revision

1. Describe the two different types of wave found at the coast.
2. Explain how headlands are formed.
3. Explain how a stump is formed.
4. Explain how a hooked spit is formed.

 Revision tip

Make sure that you learn the different coastal processes and features in detail. Exam questions often ask you to explain how features are formed.

Part 2 — Sustainable management of coasts

The need for coastal defences

Coastal defences are used to protect the coast from flooding and erosion for the following reasons:

1. People live near the coast

Across the world, many people live close to the coast. This is mostly due to the dependence on ports and transport. Also many people enjoy the view. Coastal properties often need to be protected using coastal defences, as storm surges can bring sea water inland.

2. Economic importance of the coast

Tourism at the coast is an important industry within most countries. People like to visit coastal areas for recreation, which provides many opportunities for the hospitality industry. Ports provide important transport links via ferry and cruise terminals, and allow the secure transfer and distribution of goods. This attracts many distribution, storage and processing businesses to coastal areas, as they find it beneficial to be located close to ports. New investments in offshore energy production using tidal and wave power are also on the increase. Other coastal industries such as fishing and shipbuilding have been on the decrease over recent years but they remain important in some places. All of these activities require increased protection from storms, floods and threats of sea level changes.

3. Rising sea levels due to climate change

Since 1900, sea levels have risen by about 10 cm around the UK, and 17 cm globally. This rise has been linked to climate change, which has caused global temperatures to increase and global weather patterns to change. These higher temperatures have raised sea levels by:

- warming and expanding the ocean (thermal expansion).
- melting ice, glaciers and snow, releasing water from storage.

Sea levels are expected to continue to rise and some experts estimate that the release of water from ice and snow could raise the levels around the world by up to 5 m. Even a further rise of 1 m could flood 25% of Bangladesh and other low-lying areas.

Description and evaluation of coastal management methods

Method	Description	Evaluation
Hard engineering		
Sea walls	• Usually made of concrete. • Protect the land by holding back the sea. • Wave action beats against the sea wall without eroding the coast. • Are designed to absorb and deflect wave energy.	• Expensive. • Can last for a long time. • Need deep foundations so they are not undermined by wave action. • Can be ugly. • Might not solve the erosion problem but just move it elsewhere. • Can also be used to provide walkways along the sea edge.
Groynes Longshore drift	• Wooden, concrete or rock barriers than can be built out into the sea (at a 90-degree angle). • They trap the sand carried by longshore drift to help build up a deposition beach.	• Can be cost effective but need continual maintenance and repair. • Can trap sediment, depriving the coastline further along. • Can last for up to 25 years (depending on the material they are built from).
Gabions	• Metal cages that are filled with rocks. • Are stacked together to create a wall of rock. • As waves crash against them, the energy of the water is absorbed inside the cage.	• Cheap but break apart easily. • Can be a good short-term solution. • Some see them as unattractive. • Debris and pollution can be trapped inside them creating a habitat for animals such as rats.

Method	Description	Evaluation
Soft engineering		
Beach nourishment  Source: U.S. Army Corps of Engineers photo by Cameron Siegal	• Sand or pebbles are added artificially to a beach to replenish it or build it up. • A large, wide beach can naturally protect the coastline by absorbing wave energy. • Considered a soft engineering method if the sand is brought from a sustainable source.	• Can be very expensive and require constant maintenance and protection. • Can have the least environmental consequences and works well in combination with other measures (such as groynes).
Managed retreat	• A form of land management. • Removes any form of coastal protection and allows an area that was not previously exposed to flooding and erosion to be flooded and eroded. • Usually occurs in lowland areas in river estuaries. These areas may have been reclaimed from the sea in the past.	• Very cost effective. The only cost is removing any defences already in place. • The coast will be returned to its natural state. • As the coast is eroded again, the flow of sediment will allow the build-up of beaches in the local area. • Land will be lost through the process, which means that farmers and land owners could lose their land. Compensation might be required to help with this.

 Revision tip

Make sure that you know the difference between the hard and soft engineering strategies that are used for coastal management

Case Study: Newcastle, Co Down
(a coastal management strategy from the British Isles)

Location: Newcastle, Co. Down, Northern Ireland

Sandy beaches attract tourists but sand from the 8-km-long beach was being lost due to longshore drift, leaving shingle and stones.

Shops, houses and businesses were damaged in a flood in 2002.

Why did the coast need to be managed?

The sea wall was damaged in storms (most recently in 2002).

Key tourist attractions (e.g. Royal County Down golf course) needed to be protected.

Coastal management methods used

Strategy	Description	Positive impacts	Negative impacts
Groynes	Groynes were initially built to protect the beach in the 1950s. More were built in the 1980s to collect the beach material as it was moved along the coast by longshore drift.	Stops sand being removed from the beach and builds the beach up, making the area attractive to tourists.	Groynes erode and break apart over time and can be expensive to replace. They can be unattractive and often make access to the beach difficult.
Gabions	In the 1990s, gabions were added to protect some of the sand dunes along the coast.	A good, inexpensive, short-term solution to stop erosion.	Not a long-term solution as the gabions were ineffective. Cages split under pressure from the sea and had to be replaced about 10 years later. Can be unattractive, and debris such as plastic bags and cans can collect between the stones in the cages.
Rock armour	Large rocks were used to protect the coastline from erosion.	A good, cheap solution to stop erosion.	Can provide a breeding ground for rats and other animals.
Sea wall	In 2007, over £4 million was spent redesigning the seafront. The beach had been badly eroded and a new curved sea wall was built to help protect the main street from waves and floods.	Provides two functions: • Protection for businesses and houses from flooding and large waves. • A walkway for tourists.	A very expensive solution. Had a big impact on the natural environment, completely changing the features of the place. There is concern that erosion has been shifted further along the coast.

 Revision tip

Make sure that you learn the different coastal management methods for your case study in detail. Examiners will expect you to not only refer to the methods used to protect the coast, but also explain how and why they work.

Evaluation of the coastal management techniques

- The new promenade development has won many design awards and local residents hope that this will help to rejuvenate the tourism industry.
- Concerns were raised by environmentalists about how the 'hard engineering' completely changed the face of the coastline with minimal benefit.
- Some argue that this new construction is ugly, has damaged the natural environment (and animal habitats) and has replaced natural sand dune, which is much better for beach protection.

 Revision tip

Make sure that you consider how sustainable this coastal management strategy is. What are the different social, economic and environmental factors associated with this case study? Was it value for money in the short and in the long term?

 Test your revision

1. Describe how seas walls work and evaluate their sustainability.
2. Why did the coast at Newcastle need to be managed?
3. Identify and describe which coastal management strategy you think is the most sustainable for Newcastle.

Our Changing Weather and Climate

1. Measuring the elements of the weather

2. Factors affecting climate

3. Weather systems affecting the British Isles

4. The impacts of extreme weather

| **Part 1** | ## Measuring the elements of the weather |

The difference between weather and climate

Weather: The day-to-day state of the atmosphere. It is a dynamic process that is constantly changing. The elements of the weather include temperature, precipitation, wind direction and speed, atmospheric pressure, cloud type and cloud cover.

Climate: The average weather taken over a long period of time (usually over 35 years). It is a less dynamic process and does not change as quickly as the weather.

How to measure the elements of the weather

Element	Description of element	Method of measurement	Unit	Description of equipment
Temperature	The amount of heat in the atmosphere.	Digital thermometer (instrument) 16.5 °C	Degrees centigrade (°C)	• A digital thermometer records the highest and lowest daily temperature. This can be used to calculate the range of temperature. • Thermometers should be housed in a Stevenson Screen, which allows air to circulate and protects the instrument from the heat of direct sunlight. This provides more accurate readings.
Precipitation	The amount of moisture/water in the atmosphere. This involves water in all of its states: liquid, solid and gas (vapour). It includes water, dew, hail, rain, sleet and snow.	Rain gauge (instrument)	Millimetres (mm)	• Precipitation (usually as rain) is collected in a rain gauge. • The gauge needs to be anchored so that it doesn't get blown over by the wind. • The top section should be no less than 30 cm above the ground to prevent rain splash. • The gauge should be clear of any buildings and trees as this could affect the results.

Element	Description of element	Method of measurement	Unit	Description of equipment
Wind direction	The horizontal direction of the air in motion.	Wind vane (instrument)	Eight compass points	• A wind vane shows the wind direction. It needs to be made accurately so that the arrow points into the direction of the wind. • The vane should be positioned on top of a building and avoiding shelter, as both can cause a wind tunnel.
Wind speed	How fast the air travels. The speed of wind can change from calm to hurricane force.	Anemometer (instrument)	Knots per hour (kph)	• An anemometer measures the speed of the air. • The cups are moved by the wind to indicate the exact wind speed. • Readings should be taken on top of a building and avoiding shelter. • If hand held, it must be held at full stretch above the head of the observer.
Atmospheric pressure	The pressure applied to the Earth's surface by the weight of the atmosphere. The average sea level pressure is 1013 mb. Low pressure is usually anything below this and high pressure anything above this.	Barometer (instrument)	Millibars (mb)	An aneroid barometer can be used to measure pressure. If pressure is rising or falling this will help indicate how the weather is likely to change.
Cloud type	A cloud is a visible mass of tiny water droplets floating in the atmosphere. It consists of water formed from the condensation of water vapour. Clouds are split into categories based on their shape and height.	Observation	Stratus, cumulus, cumulonimbus, cirrus	Clouds are found at one of three layers in the sky: low, middle or high.
Cloud cover	The amount of sky covered by cloud.	Observation	Oktas (eighths)	An observer will estimate the amount of blue sky that is visible and identify how much of the sky is covered by cloud.

The main cloud types

Stratus: These are layered clouds that are usually quite low in the sky. They are flat, featureless and often grey in colour, and bring light drizzle or small amounts of snow.

Cumulus: These clouds seem to move fast. They are white, have a fluffy appearance and can bring rain.

Cumulonimbus: Towering clouds that bring moisture. They start to tower as air rises and can bring hail, thunder and lightning.

Cirrus: These are very high wispy clouds. They are usually made up of ice particles.

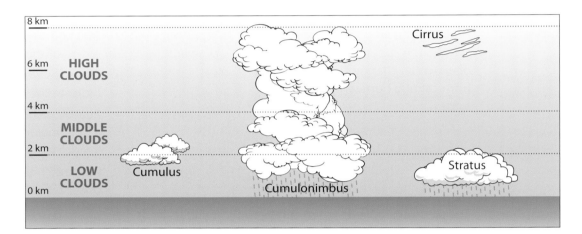

 Revision tip

Make sure that you know:
- how to measure/observe the seven weather elements.
- what to consider when locating weather instruments.

Sources of data used to create a weather forecast

 Key geographical terms

Weather forecast: A prediction of how the weather is likely to change over the next few days and how this will affect people (e.g. what clothes to wear).

Meteorologists use computers to analyse current data and previous weather patterns to predict future weather. The weather data is collected from the following sources:

1. On land

- **Land-based weather stations**
  Across the UK there are 30 major weather observation stations staffed by professional meteorologists who take observations every hour. There are an additional 100 auxiliary stations manned by coastguards, along with another 100 or so fully-automated stations.

- **Rainfall radar**
  A type of pulse-Doppler radar is used to locate the amount of precipitation in the atmosphere. The intensity of the precipitation is measured to calculate the density of the rainfall and the potential for storms or severe weather.

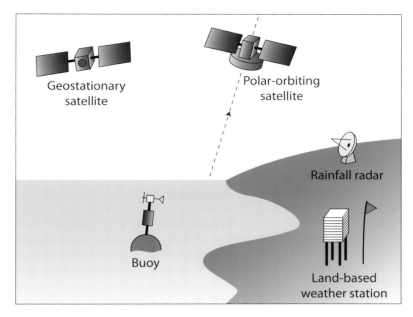

2. In the air – satellites

Satellites are small spacecraft that orbit the Earth and record the weather. They help to give a 'big picture' of what is happening in the atmosphere. Satellites use radiometers to measure radiation across different wavelengths. They help find detailed cloud formations using visible light images (in daylight), and less-detailed infrared images (both during the day and at night).

- **Geostationary satellites:** hover over the same spot on the Earth, moving at the speed of the Earth's rotation. They usually remain over the equator at an altitude of 36,000 km, e.g. the European Meteosat.

- **Polar-orbiting satellites:** travel around the Earth from pole to pole at a height of 850 km. They pass the same point on the Earth every 12 hours. These satellites provide pictures of the clouds and information about the temperature, e.g. the US NOAA satellites.

3. At sea – buoys

Moored and floating (drifting) buoys are used to record weather information and send it back to weather centres. They usually record air temperature, wind speed, atmospheric pressure and wind direction, and sometimes water temperature, wave height and wave period. They transmit data back to meteorologists using satellite communications.

 Test your revision

1. What is the difference between weather and climate?
2. What are the seven elements of the weather?
3. Describe how to accurately measure temperature and precipitation in the atmosphere.
4. Explain some of the factors that need to be considered when positioning a rain gauge.
5. Describe the main sources of weather data that could be used to create a weather forecast.
6. What is the difference between a geostationary satellite and polar-orbiting satellite?

Part 2 Factors affecting climate

Climate is the average weather taken over a long period of time (usually over 35 years). The climate of a particular place does not change much over a short period of time. Climate is affected by a range of physical factors which means that it varies widely around the world.

1. Latitude

The closer a place is to the equator, the warmer it will be. The closer a place is to the North and South Poles, the colder it will be. The curve of the Earth means that heat is concentrated at the equator and much less towards the poles.

How latitude can impact climate

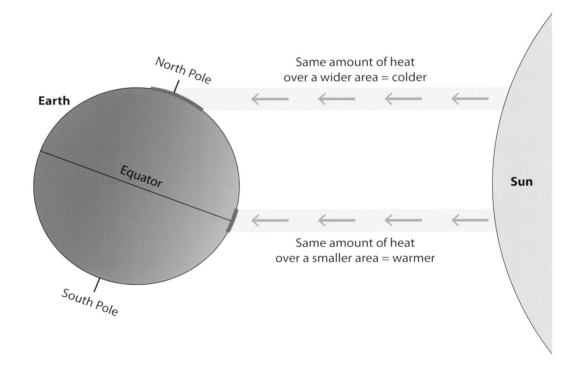

2. Prevailing winds

The prevailing wind is the most common wind direction for a location. Prevailing winds for the British Isles are west to south-westerly, which bring a mild, damp climate.

3. Distance from the sea

Water heats up slowly and cools down slowly, whereas land heats up quickly and cools down quickly. This means that water retains heat for much longer periods than land. For this reason, in summer it will be warmer inland than at the coast, as the land heats up more quickly. In winter it will be warmer at the coast than inland, as the sea cools down more slowly. This is why coastal areas have a smaller annual temperature range than inland areas.

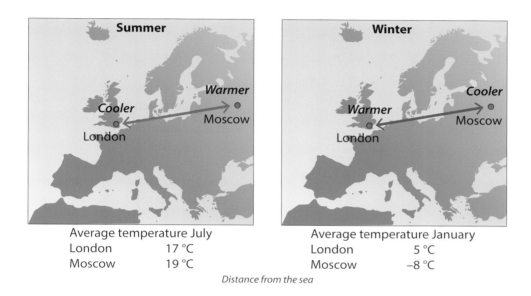

Average temperature July		Average temperature January	
London	17 °C	London	5 °C
Moscow	19 °C	Moscow	−8 °C

Distance from the sea

4. Altitude

Places that are high up will be much colder than areas that are low down. Within the atmosphere, for each 100 m of altitude, the temperature will fall by around 1 °C due to adiabatic cooling. This means that on hills and mountains the temperature will be much lower at the top than at the bottom. Wind chill factor can also further reduce the temperature at the top.

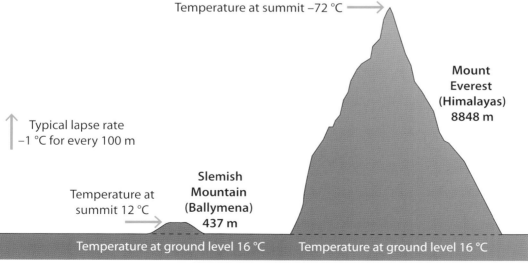

How altitude can impact climate

Part 3 — Weather systems affecting the British Isles

Air masses affecting the British Isles

 Key geographical terms

Air mass: A body of air with similar temperature and moisture characteristics, which is often thousands of kilometres wide.

Polar maritime (Pm)

- This is a common air mass affecting the British Isles.
- *Temperature:* It originates over the north Atlantic Ocean and brings cold air from the Arctic north. It reaches the British Isles from the north west.
- *Moisture:* It produces cumulus and cumulonimbus clouds but has good visibility between showers.
- *Seasonal variation:* It brings frequent showers at any time of year.

Tropical maritime (Tm)

- This is a very common air mass affecting the British Isles.
- *Temperature:* It brings warm air from the mid-Atlantic Ocean and moves over the south west of the British Isles.
- *Moisture:* It is responsible for bringing dull skies (nimbostratus clouds), drizzle and fog (poor visibility).
- *Seasonal variation:* It brings mild conditions in the winter and warm weather in the summer.

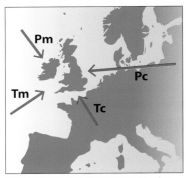

Air masses affecting the British Isles

Polar continental (Pc)

- This is more common in winter than summer in the British Isles
- *Temperature:* It originates over Eastern Europe and Russia, and brings cold, dry air from the east/north east.
- *Moisture:* In winter it can bring snow showers along the east coast of England.
- *Seasonal variation:* In winter it brings very cold, snowy conditions. In summer it brings dry, cool conditions.

Tropical continental (Tc)

- This is the least common air mass affecting the British Isles. It usually occurs in the summer.
- *Temperature:* Its air travels from North Africa, bringing very warm and dry air from the south and south east.
- *Moisture:* It can cause thunderstorms to develop if the temperatures rise.
- *Seasonal variation:* It is most common in the summer months, when it brings hot weather (heat waves). When it occurs at other times of year, it brings mild conditions.

Revision tip

Make sure that you know the difference between the four main air masses. Exam questions often test your knowledge of their specific temperature and moisture characteristics, and seasonal variations.

Weather patterns

Across the British Isles there are two separate weather systems that control our weather:

1. **Depression:** A low pressure system associated with unsettled weather and bands of wind, rain, and even snow in winter.

2. **Anticyclone:** A high pressure system associated with settled weather and usually cloudless skies.

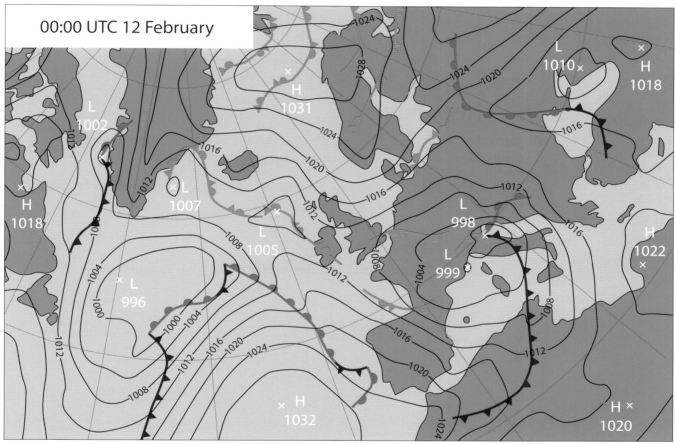

A Met Office surface pressure chart for 12 February

The influence of pressure and wind

Surface pressure charts are often used to record atmospheric pressure. Isobars are the black lines used to join places with the same atmospheric pressure. When isobars are close together this indicates increased pressure and strong winds. When isobars are further apart this indicates gentle winds.

How weather fronts are formed

Front: A boundary between two air masses with different temperatures and characteristics.

Cold front: The boundary between an advancing cold air mass and a warm air mass. It brings a change in weather and a narrow belt of rain and clouds.

Warm front: The boundary between an advancing warm air mass and a cold air mass. It brings a belt of cloud and some rain. The rain will gradually increase as the front gets closer.

Weather charts

A synoptic chart: A weather map that gives a snapshot of the weather across a region. It summarises a large amount of complicated, detailed information.

A surface chart: A chart containing all the information recorded from surface weather observations or automated sites.

Weather observation

The weather taken at a particular weather station could look like this:

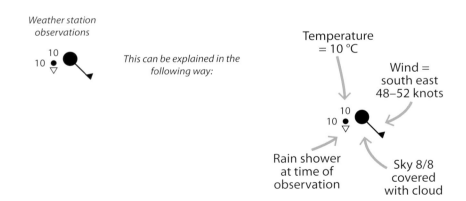

The symbols are explained below:

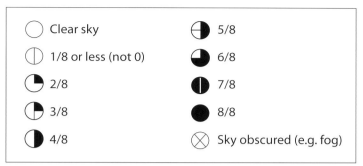

Cloud cover

The circle that shows the weather centre also shows the observed cloud cover.

Precipitation

The type of precipitation is usually shown underneath the temperature measurement.

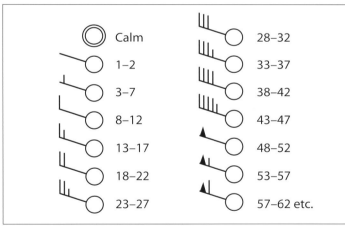

Wind speed

The wind speed is usually recorded as a 'shaft', which also points to the direction where the wind is coming from. The 'feathers' on the end of the shaft show the speed of the wind.

 Test your revision

1. What is an air mass?
2. What are the main differences between the four main air masses?
3. Describe the weather you would expect if tropical maritime was the most dominant air mass.
4. How can you tell wind speed on a surface/synoptic chart using isobars?

Frontal depressions across the British Isles

⭐ **Key geographical terms**

Frontal depression: An area of low atmospheric pressure that produces cloudy, rainy and windy weather.

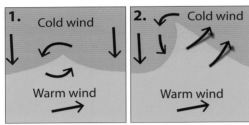

The formation of a depression

The formation of a depression

In the UK, a depression is formed out in the Atlantic Ocean when cold, polar maritime air from the north moves south and meets some warm, tropical maritime air from the south. The lighter, warm air will start to rise up over the denser, cold air and will develop into a front.

The passage of a depression

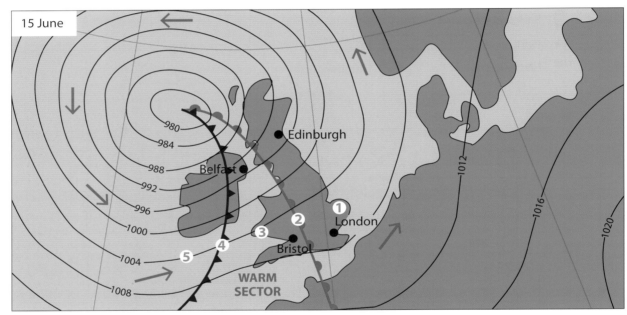

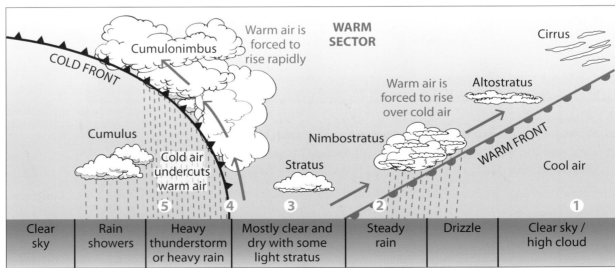

Clear sky	Rain showers	Heavy thunderstorm or heavy rain	Mostly clear and dry with some light stratus	Steady rain	Drizzle	Clear sky / high cloud

Weather will change as a depression moves overhead. Imagine you are standing at position 1 on the diagrams. You will experience the following sequence of weather:

1. **Ahead of the warm front:** The depression has not arrived yet. Pressure is falling, temperature is steady and there are cirrus clouds high in the sky. Gradually, cloud cover increases and the cloud descends and thickens becoming altostratus.

2. **At the warm front:** Warm air is forced to rise over cold air. As the warm air rises, it cools, condenses and forms clouds. Pressure continues to fall, wind speed increases slightly and temperature rises. Nimbostratus clouds are low and cover the sky. Drizzle turns to steady rain.

3. **Warm sector:** Pressure is low and steady, temperature is mild and there is a steady breeze. There are breaks in the cloud and a little drizzle but nothing heavy. Weather can be settled but it doesn't last long.

4. **At the cold front:** The weather changes dramatically. Cold air undercuts the warm air in the warm sector, forcing the warm air to rise rapidly. This causes towering cumulonimbus clouds to form, bringing heavy rain and possibly thunder and lightning. Pressure starts to rise, temperature falls and there are strong winds. Rain and any thunderstorms will clear as the front moves away.

5. **The depression moves away:** Pressure continues to rise and the temperature remains cold. The clouds thin out but cumulus result in a few showers. The strong winds die down but there is still some wind.

 Revision tip

Make sure that you know how to describe the sequence of weather at:
- the warm front
- the warm sector
- the cold front

Anticyclones in the British Isles during the summer and winter

 Key geographical terms

Anticyclone: An area of high pressure that is usually bigger than an depression. It produces calm, settled weather with little cloud cover or precipitation.

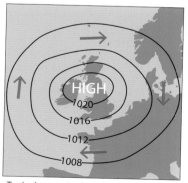
Typical synoptic chart for an anticyclone

Air in an anticyclone sinks from high altitude. As it descends, it absorbs any moisture and stops condensation from taking place, which restricts cloud formation. Winds tend to be light and blow in a clockwise direction around the high pressure. This all results in settled weather with few clouds and clear skies. Summer weather is usually dry and warm. In winter, the light winds and clear skies can lead to overnight fog or frost. Anticyclones are large, powerful weather systems that can stay in place for long periods of time. If an anticyclone stays over northern Europe in winter then the British Isles can experience very cold east winds.

Key features of depressions and anticyclones

Note: The formation and features of an anticyclone are largely the same in summer and winter but the impacts can be different.

	Depressions	Summer anticyclone	Winter anticyclone
Pressure	Low and falling (below 1000 mb).	High and increasing (over 1000 mb).	High and increasing (over 1000 mb).
Temperature	Temperatures vary depending on the type of air that is passing overhead.	Long, sunny days and lack of clouds lead to warm temperatures. These can reach 24 °C or even higher. At night, temperatures drop rapidly as clear skies mean that heat escapes back into the atmosphere.	Lack of cloud cover allows daily temperatures to increase. At night, temperatures drop rapidly as heat escapes back into the atmosphere.
Cloud cover	A wide and varied selection of clouds can be found as a depression passes.	Sinking air means there are settled conditions with few clouds and clear skies.	Sinking air means that there are settled conditions with few clouds and clear skies.
Wind speed and direction	Isobars are close together, which indicates strong winds. Winds blow in an anticlockwise direction. A depression usually passes in a north-east direction and will take between three to five days to pass over the British Isles.	Isobars are far apart, which indicates light winds and calm conditions. Wind direction is clockwise around the high pressure.	Isobars are far apart, which indicates light winds and calm conditions. Wind direction is clockwise around the high pressure.
Precipitation	Precipitation will vary, including snow in winter and a lot of rain over a three to five day period. As the cold front passes, this can bring thunderstorms and lightning (especially in the summer).	Normally dry weather. Little or no precipitation during the day but clear skies can bring dew and fog, especially in the mornings. Thunderstorms can be triggered on hot days as convectional rainfall.	Very little direct precipitation. The clear, settled conditions can lead to frost and fog. Light winds and low temperatures can lead to fog remaining well into the following morning.

Limitations of forecasting (range and accuracy)

A weather forecast is a prediction of how the weather is likely to change over time. Weather forecasters use satellite images along with lots of other information to help to work out what the weather in a particular location is likely to be over the next few days.

Range: This is the amount of time in advance that a weather forecast can be made with a high level of accuracy. The UKMET (UK Meteorological office) weather model can help to predict the weather for up to six days in advance. Generally short-range weather forecasts are more accurate than long-range forecasts.

Accuracy: No weather forecast can be 100% accurate, as there are too many variables that can influence the local weather, including the surfaces that the weather passes over, the temperature, the microclimate and the size of a settlement.

The impacts of extreme weather

Extreme weather

Extreme weather is when a weather event brings weather features that are significantly different from what is typical for an area. Examples include drought, tornadoes and hurricanes.

Hurricanes

A **hurricane** is a tropical revolving storm (an intense rotating depression). It is also called a tropical cyclone or typhoon, depending on where in the world it forms. Hurricanes occur when the wind speeds are above 115 km per hour and the atmospheric pressure is extremely low (below 970 mb). The extreme wind speeds and amount of precipitation cause flooding and damage to people and property.

How hurricanes are formed

Hurricanes occur in late summer and autumn in the northern hemisphere. They usually track from east to west and will spin away from the equator.

Hurricanes usually become vast weather systems that can span over 1000 km. Each hurricane can grow to over 12 km high, with an eye that can increase to around 50 km wide. A hurricane's power source is warm water, so when a hurricane hits land it will quickly lose intensity and wind speed.

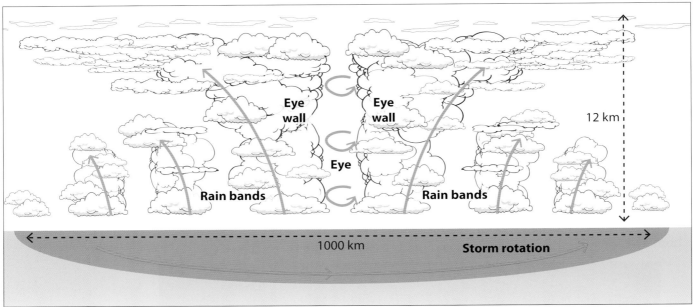

Cross section of a hurricane

The impacts of extreme weather (hurricanes) on people and property

The main hazards that a hurricane can bring are:

1. **Storm surges:** This is when the hurricane's low air pressure causes sea levels to rise abnormally. High winds force the sea water onto the land, causing flooding and damage to property.

2. **Flooding:** Heavy rain can cause flooding hundreds of miles inland. Flood water can remain for a long time after the hurricane has passed, as the ground is saturated and the water cannot drain away.

3. **Hurricane-force winds:** These can destroy homes, buildings and damage any poorly-built structures.

Case Study: Hurricane Katrina, USA
(a Hurricane event outside the British Isles)

Location: USA | **Date: 29 August 2005**

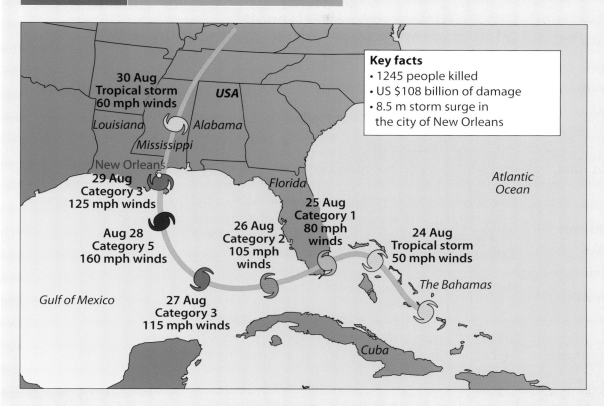

Key facts
- 1245 people killed
- US $108 billion of damage
- 8.5 m storm surge in the city of New Orleans

On 23 August 2005, a depression in the Atlantic Ocean quickly intensified into a hurricane. An estimated 1245 people died in the hurricane and the flooding that followed. The amount of damage was estimated at around $108 billion.

The hurricane moved across the Bahamas, hitting the Florida coast on 25 August. It then crossed the Gulf of Mexico and reached New Orleans on 29 August.

Main features

1. **Storm surge:** An 8.5 m high coastal surge of water was caused by the large waves and high winds. It caused flooding across New Orleans and breached the levee system. Over 80% of the city was flooded and the flood waters were able to reach 19 km inland.

2. **Rainfall:** A large amount of rainfall caused flooding before the hurricane even hit landfall. The peak rainfall levels measured over 250 mm in a 24-hour period.

3. **High wind speeds:** Hurricane Katrina made Category 5 on 28 August, and winds of over 280 km/h were recorded over the Gulf of Mexico (along with an atmospheric pressure of 902 mb). The winds dropped slightly to 200 km/h when the hurricane hit landfall in Louisiana.

Impact on people

Deaths	FEMA (the Federal Emergency Management Agency in the USA) recorded the death toll as 1836 people.
Homeless	Over 500,000 people were listed as homeless. 273,000 people were housed in emergency shelters and later FEMA trailers housed over 114,000 people.
Electricity	Over 3 million people were left without electricity.
Water supply	Drinking water supplies along the Gulf Coast were polluted with sewage for many months.
Education	18 schools were destroyed and a further 74 schools were badly damaged.
Economic	Over 230,000 jobs were lost as businesses were completely destroyed and people could not return to work quickly. Many people remained unemployed over 10 years later. The total damage is estimated at $108 billion – making hurricane Katrina the costliest hurricane event in history.
Health	People were most concerned about the contamination of water due to sewage, refuse and dead bodies.
Law and order	In the immediate aftermath of the hurricane event, the city experienced looting and other crime. The US military had to patrol the streets of New Orleans to restore law and order.

Impact on property

Flooding	Over 80% of New Orleans was flooded – mostly the residential sections of the city, which were flooded up to 3 m. A major cause was the failure of the levees and flood walls to protect New Orleans.
Housing	A million housing units were damaged along the Gulf Coast. Over 300,000 houses were destroyed by Hurricane Katrina. In New Orleans alone, 134,000 houses were damaged (70% of the total).
Storm debris	In some places within New Orleans, storm debris remained until 2010. Even today, there are still some vacant homes that require building work to make them habitable again.
Rebuilding	Six months after the hurricane, the city of New Orleans still did not have a working sewage system or gas and electricity supplies. It took time to provide basic services so that people could return to their homes and start rebuilding.

 Revision tip

It is important that you learn some key facts and figures to support your case study answers. Exam questions often ask you to describe the impact of the extreme weather event on people or on property. You need to be prepared for both.

 Test your revision

1. Describe the main causes of a hurricane.
2. Outline the main impacts that an extreme weather event might have on people.
3. Describe the main impact on property of an extreme weather event outside the British Isles.

The Restless Earth

1. Plate tectonics theory
2. Basic rock types
3. Managing earthquakes
4. Volcanoes: characteristics and consequences

Part 1 | Plate tectonics theory

The structure of the Earth

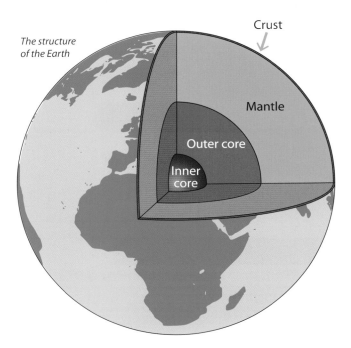

The structure of the Earth

Crust
Mantle
Outer core
Inner core

The distance from the edge of the crust to the centre of the Earth is 6370 km.

The inner and outer cores: are layers at the centre of the Earth, with temperatures of over 6000 °C. The material there is much denser than at the crust. The outer core is 1200 km thick and the inner core is 2200 km thick.

The mantle: is the thickest layer of the Earth (2900 km thick). It is made up of silicate rocks that remain molten and can move about.

The crust: is the thin layer in the outermost section of the Earth. It ranges from 5–70 km in thickness. It is broken up into several large sections known as plates.

The Earth's crust, plates and movement

The theory of plate tectonics helps us understand what is happening beneath our feet. The Earth's hard crustal rock sits on a layer of molten mantle rock. Plate tectonics theory states that the crust is divided into sections called tectonic plates. There are seven major plates (North American, Pacific, South American, Antarctic, African, Eurasian and Indo-Australian Plates) and other minor plates (which include the Nazca, Cocos, Caribbean, Arabian and Philippine Plates). The plates are constantly moving around on top of the mantle. The places where plates meet are known as plate margins. Scientists note that increased tectonic activity (earthquakes or volcanoes) takes place at the boundaries or margins of plates.

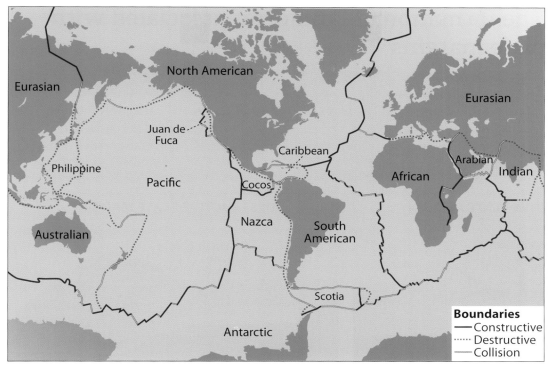

World plate boundaries

Boundaries
— Constructive
····· Destructive
— Collision

How convection currents cause plate movement

1. The rock melts inside the thick layer of mantle. As the rock becomes molten, it becomes less dense than the material above it and rises towards the surface.

2. The molten rock (magma) rises and some escapes through cracks in the crust. This escaping magma creates new volcanoes.

3. Any excess magma starts to cool, becomes denser and sinks deeper into the mantle.

4. The magma is reheated and starts the cycle again.

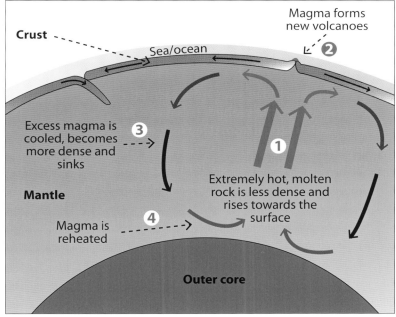

Convection currents in the mantle

Plate types

There are two different types of plate:

Continental plates	Oceanic plates
• 35–100 km (thick)	• 6–10 km (thin)
• Form the major land masses/continents	• Form the ocean beds
• Rocks can be very old	• Rocks can be very young
• Generally contain 'light' rocks that are less dense	• Generally contain 'heavy' rocks that are more dense
• Example: Granite	• Example: Basalt

The formation of landforms associated with plate margins

★	Key geographical terms

Plate margin/boundary: The place where two plates meet. Plates rarely move at consistent speeds; some plates move regularly whilst others have not moved in centuries. The boundaries include constructive, destructive and conservative plate margins, and collision zone.

CONSTRUCTIVE PLATE MARGIN	DESTRUCTIVE PLATE MARGIN

Movement	Plates move apart	Movement	A continental and an oceanic plate move towards each other

Description
- As two plates move away from each other, they create a gap in the seabed. This gap is filled with fresh material from deep inside the Earth (mid-ocean ridge).
- Underwater volcanoes are formed, some of which continue to grow with every eruption until they form small islands.
- When plates move, this can sometimes trigger earthquakes.

Description
- Plates move because of convection currents in the mantle.
- The denser oceanic crust plate moves towards the lighter but thicker continental crust plate, and the oceanic plate is forced underneath.
- This creates a deep ocean trench and a subduction zone, where earthquakes can be felt.
- As the oceanic plate sinks, the plate is heated by the mantle and begins to melt. The melted oceanic crust is less dense (lighter) than the mantle so it rises and causes violent volcanic eruptions at composite cone volcanoes.

Landforms	Mid-ocean ridge and volcanoes	Landforms	Subduction zone and ocean trench
Example	Mid-Atlantic ridge, Iceland	Example	Andes Mountains, west coast of South America

COLLISION ZONE		CONSERVATIVE PLATE MARGIN	
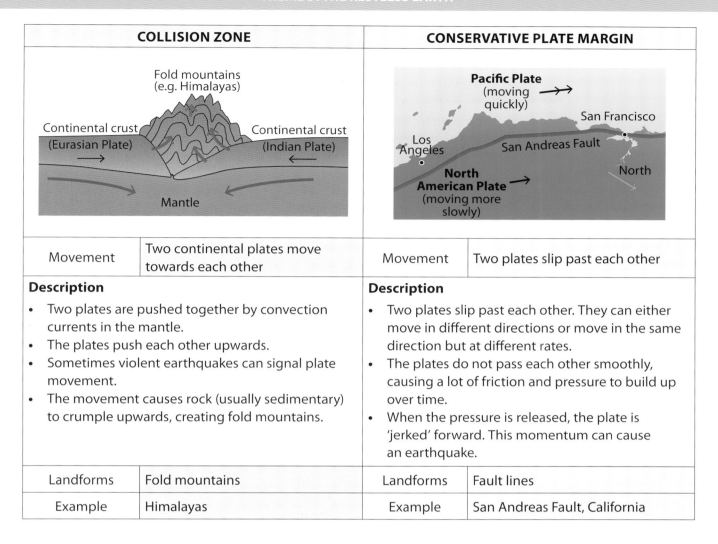			
Movement	Two continental plates move towards each other	Movement	Two plates slip past each other

Description

- Two plates are pushed together by convection currents in the mantle.
- The plates push each other upwards.
- Sometimes violent earthquakes can signal plate movement.
- The movement causes rock (usually sedimentary) to crumple upwards, creating fold mountains.

Description

- Two plates slip past each other. They can either move in different directions or move in the same direction but at different rates.
- The plates do not pass each other smoothly, causing a lot of friction and pressure to build up over time.
- When the pressure is released, the plate is 'jerked' forward. This momentum can cause an earthquake.

Landforms	Fold mountains	Landforms	Fault lines
Example	Himalayas	Example	San Andreas Fault, California

 Revision tip

Learn the reasons for the tectonic movements of all four different types of plate boundary. Exam questions could ask you to show detailed knowledge of any of the four types.

 Test your revision

1. Describe the main features of the core and the crust.
2. How can convection currents cause plates to move?
3. What is the difference between continental and oceanic plates?
4. Explain the landforms at a constructive plate margin.

Part 2   Basic rock types

There are many different kinds of rocks. They are classified by how they were made, how they were changed and what they are made from. All rocks can be classified as igneous, sedimentary or metamorphic.

Igneous rocks (basalt and granite): Rocks formed when molten rock (magma) from underneath the Earth's crust cools and hardens. This molten rock is called lava on the surface of the Earth. There are usually crystals evident in the rock, unless the rock cools quickly and the lava hardens on the surface (e.g. basalt, which has very small crystals).

Basalt

Granite

Sedimentary rocks (limestone and sandstone): Rocks formed by sediment that has built up over a long period of time, usually under water. The sediment is made up of weathered and eroded material that builds up in layers. As more and more material is added, pressure pushes air and water out, and the sediment becomes cemented into a rock.

Sandstone

Limestone

Metamorphic rocks (slate and marble): Rocks that have changed from an earlier state through the addition of pressure or heat. Originally, these rocks were igneous or sedimentary (e.g. marble is a metamorphic rock that was once limestone, a sedimentary rock).

Marble

Slate

 Revision tip

Make sure you can name examples of each rock type and explain how they are formed.

 Test your revision

1. Name the three main rock types.
2. Explain how metamorphic rocks are formed.

Part 3 Managing earthquakes

The global distribution and causes of earthquakes

⭐ **Key geographical terms**

Earthquake: A shaking of the Earth's crust due to the movement of the Earth's plates.

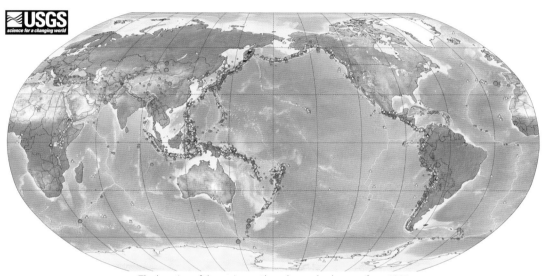

The location of the major earthquakes and volcanoes from 1900

KEY

Depth of focus
- 0–69 km
- 70–299 km
- 300–700 km

Active volcano
△

Plate boundary

⭐ **Revision tip**
Make sure that you use geographical language (north/south/east/west) and mention continents and countries when describing global earthquake distribution.

The global distribution of earthquakes is closely connected to the position of plate boundaries. It is rare for earthquakes to take place anywhere else. Generally:
- earthquakes occur in narrow belts at plate margins.
- they occur on all four types of plate margins.
- the most powerful earthquakes are associated with destructive, collision and conservative plate margins.
- earthquakes at constructive plate boundaries tend to be weaker than earthquakes at destructive, collision or conservative plate boundaries.

The focus and epicentre of an earthquake

- The **focus** is the place where the earthquake originally occurs.
- Seismic waves (vibrations) travel from the focus to the surface.
- The **epicentre** is the point on the Earth's surface directly above the focus. It is where the shock waves are first felt at the surface.

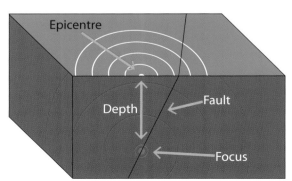

Features of an earthquake

Earthquake magnitude is measured on a seismograph using the Richter scale

- Seismic waves can be recorded using a **seismograph** (a weight with a pen attached, which is suspended from a spring).
- The strength of an earthquake (its magnitude) is measured on the Richter scale. This is a logarithmic scale, which means that a magnitude 6.0 earthquake is 10 times greater than a magnitude 5.0 earthquake.

Magnitude	Effects
Less than 3.0	• Rarely felt, only detected by seismographs.
3.0–3.9	• Sometimes vibrations felt, but rarely causes damage.
4.0–4.9	• Some rattling. • Some shaking of indoor items. • Might break windows or cause unstable objects to fall.
5.0–5.9	• Can cause major damage to poorly-built buildings. • Slight damage to well-designed buildings. • Furniture will be moved.
6.0–6.9	• Can be destructive in urban areas.
7.0–7.9	• Can cause serious damage over a large area. • Buildings can be moved from foundations. • Cracks in the earth. • Pipes break.
8.0–8.9	• Causes damage over a very wide area. • Buildings are destroyed and few structures are left standing.
9.0–9.9	• Devastating over an extremely wide area. Near total destruction.
More than 10	• Never recorded but impact would be catastrophic.

The physical consequences of earthquakes

Liquefaction

Liquefaction occurs when an earthquake hits an area and shakes the wet soil. The shaking causes the water within the soil to rise to the surface, turning the soil into liquid mud. Buildings, roads and bridges start to sink, as the liquid mud cannot support the weight of these structures.

Tsunami

A tsunami is a large wave that is created when an underwater earthquake sends shockwaves through the water. This causes a surge of water to move towards the coastline. Often the energy transferred from a tsunami can travel for thousands of miles across the oceans.

How a tsunami happens

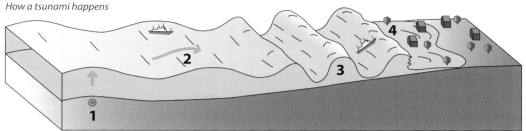

1. A rupture in the sea floor pushes water upwards and starts the waves moving.

2. The waves move rapidly across the deep ocean, reaching speeds of up to 500 km/h.

3. As the waves near land, they slow to 45 km/h but get squeezed upwards by the sloping beach. The waves start to increase in height.

4. The waves climb to 10–40 m in height and move inland, destroying everything in their way.

Case study: Causes, impacts and evaluation of the management responses to the Great Tohoku Earthquake, Japan, 11 March 2011 (an MEDC case study)

Date:	11 March 2011
Time:	14:46
Location:	Off the coast of Japan
Epicentre:	43 miles east of Tohoku
Magnitude:	9.0 undersea earthquake
Depth:	20 miles
Lasted:	6 minutes
Tsunami:	Wave height 40.5 m, travelled 6 miles inland

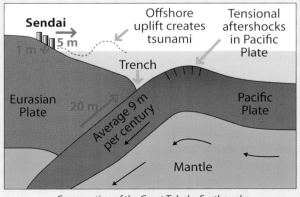

The plate boundaries affecting Japan

Cross section of the Great Tohoku Earthquake

Identify the plates involved

- Japan lies on a destructive plate boundary, where both the Philippine and Pacific Plates (oceanic) move towards the Eurasian and North American Plates (continental).

- A large amount of friction was built up over time, causing the Pacific Plate to be subducted beneath the Eurasian Plate.

Short-term impacts (on people and the environment)

ON PEOPLE

Death and injury: 15,894 people died, 6152 people were injured and 130,927 were displaced.

Defences ineffective: Japan had spent billions of dollars on tsunami defences but a 40 m high tsunami wave washed over them. Water moved up to 6 miles inland, destroying houses, factories and roads, and killing thousands of people.

Damage: 332,395 buildings, 2126 roads, 56 bridges and 26 railways were destroyed or damaged. 300 hospitals were damaged and 11 were destroyed. 23,000 vehicles were damaged. Ports were closed for three weeks. One dam ruptured and cracks were found in another six.

Nuclear crisis: The Fukushima nuclear plant was protected by a 5 m high tsunami barrier, yet a 9 m wave came ashore and flooded the plant's generators.

Power supplies: 4.4 million households in North-East Japan lost electricity. Power blackouts occurred in some areas for up to three months.

ON THE ENVIRONMENT

Fore and aftershocks: A number of foreshocks were measured (some up to 7.2 on the Richter scale) plus hundreds of aftershocks. Three measured more than magnitude 6 and another three at magnitude 7. An estimated 800 earthquakes rocked the area,

which created fissures in the ground and caused damage.

Tsunami: The wave also travelled east towards Alaska and Chile. The flooding caused by the wave damaged buildings, caused pollution and affected drinking water.

Land subsidence: Some coastal areas experienced subsidence. The beachfront dropped by 50 cm and made the area even more prone to flooding.

Long-term impacts (on people and the environment)

ON PEOPLE

Economy: The World Bank estimated a cost of US $235 billion for the damage. Parts of Japan are still in the process of being rebuilt.

Tsunami: Only 58% of people living in coastal areas heeded tsunami warnings to head for higher ground. The water hit 49% of the people who did not.

Nuclear energy: Earthquake damage caused the meltdown of seven reactors. This lead to the evacuation of areas affecting over 200,000 people. Radiation at one time was eight times normal levels. Radioactive water and leaks contaminated soil and food over a wide area. The incident damaged confidence in the safety of nuclear energy and protests caused all

Japanese nuclear reactors to be taken offline until June 2012.

Transport: Japan's transport network was severely disrupted. Sections of the Tohoku expressway were damaged and Sendai airport was hit by the Tsunami wave. Four trains were derailed and 1100 sections of rail line needed repaired.

ON THE ENVIRONMENT

Landmass movement: The quake moved North-East Japan 2.4 m closer to North America, making parts of the Japanese island landmass wider than before.

Coastline movement: A 250-mile stretch of coastline dropped by 0.6 m, allowing the tsunami wave to travel further inland.

Liquefaction: Liquefaction occurred in many areas. Thirty homes were destroyed and 1046 buildings were damaged in this way.

Aftershocks: Japan measured over 900 aftershocks following the earthquake, some of which were over magnitude 7.

Antarctica: Some seismic waves were reported to have caused large slabs of ice to fall from the Sulzberger Ice Shelf.

Evaluation of how the country prepared for and responded to the earthquake

PREDICTION AND PRECAUTIONS	
PREPARED FOR THE EARTHQUAKE	**RESPONDED TO THE EARTHQUAKE**
Earthquake prediction: Japan has spent over £70 million trying to predict earthquakes before they happen. They use lasers to measure possible Earth movements.	**Refugees:** The earthquake created over 300,000 refugees and resulted in shortages of food, water, shelter, medicine and fuel for survivors. *(Immediate response)*
National Disaster Prevention Day: Every year, on 1 September, the Japanese government holds earthquake and tsunami drills.	**Aid:** Aid organisations in Japan and worldwide responded to the disaster. The Japanese Red Cross reported over $1 billion in donations (many from overseas). *(Immediate and long-term response)*
Earthquake-proof buildings: Japan spends billions of pounds on buildings that are designed to be resistant to the effects of earthquakes.	**Rebuilding:** The Japanese Government announced that more than 23 trillion Yen over the next 10 years would be made available to aid rebuilding programmes. The government also agreed to build even stronger 'earthquake-proof' houses that could withstand more powerful earthquakes. *(Long-term response)*
Early warning systems: The tsunami warning system in Japan was set up in 1952 with 300 sensors. Tsunami safety has been a focus for coastal city planning throughout the nation. Hundreds of earthquake-proof and tsunami-proof shelters have been constructed, and some cities have built tsunami walls and floodgates to stop waves from travelling inland through river systems.	**Tsunami barriers:** Almost 400 km of sea walls have been built to help protect coastal communities from future tsunamis. There are plans for some to be as high as 18 m around valuable sites (such as nuclear power stations). *(Long-term response)*
	Economic factors: Industrial companies (such as carmakers Toyota and Honda) were encouraged to rebuild and restart production as quickly as possible. This was challenging as factories were flooded and without a reliable power supply. Damaged infrastructure links also made it difficult to import components and export finished products. *(Long-term response)*

 Revision tip

You need to know the details behind the earthquake case study.
- Learn the causes of the earthquake, and both the short- and long-term impacts on people and the environment. You must be able to write an in-depth answer on impacts.
- You also need to evaluate how the country prepared for and responded to the earthquake: Were the preparations adequate? How good were the responses to the earthquake after the event? Was it surprising that a rich country like Japan needed a lot of support from other MEDCs?

 Test your revision

1. Explain how an earthquake is measured.
2. Distinguish between the focus and epicentre of an earthquake.
3. How can liquefaction happen during an earthquake?
4. Describe the causes of the MEDC earthquake that hit Japan in 2011.
5. Explain two impacts of the MEDC earthquake on people.

Part 4 — Volcanoes – characteristics and consequences

Volcano: Where lava, ash and gas erupts through a vent in the crust.

Composite volcano: A cone-shaped volcano, with quite steep volcano sides (usually between 30° and 40°), made up of alternating layers of hardened ash and lava.

Shield volcano: A cone-shaped volcano, with gently-sloping flanks (usually less than 10°), made up of runny lava flows that harden on top of each other.

Supervolcano: A large volcano that is capable of causing a caldera-forming 'super eruption'. It has the potential of erupting at least 1000 km³ of material that could have global consequences.

Volcano characteristics

A volcano is formed by the upward movement of magma pushing through cracks in the crust. Lava, ash and gas erupts from a vent in the Earth's surface and solidifies. This can sometimes form a mountain. An active volcano is one that has erupted recently (within the last 10,000 years). A dormant volcano is one that has not erupted for a long time ('sleeping'). An extinct volcano is one that scientists think will be unlikely to erupt again as it no longer has a magma supply.

Composite volcanoes

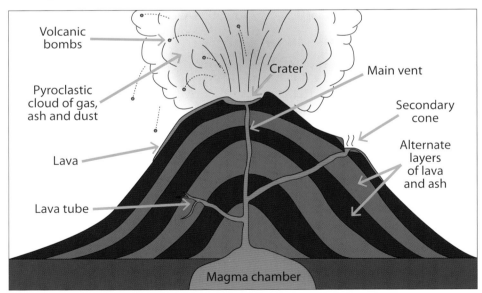

Features of a composite volcano

A composite volcano is cone-shaped, with quite steep volcano flanks (sides) (usually between 30° and 40°). It is made up of alternating layers of hardened volcanic ash and lava, which built up over a long period of time. The volcano is fed by a main vent that moves magma from deep inside the Earth, often gathering in a magma chamber before it is forced towards the surface. The magma is usually quite viscous (thick) and traps gases that can cause great explosions in an eruption event. Volcanoes like this can produce lava, volcanic bombs (tephra), gas, steam, ash and dust. Extreme eruptions can sometimes cause a pyroclastic flow – a fast-moving wave of hot gas (over 1000 °C) and eruptive material that will move down the mountainside at up to 700 km/h. Mount St Helens in the USA, Mount Pinatubo in the Philippines and Mount Fuji in Japan are examples of this type of volcano.

Shield volcanoes

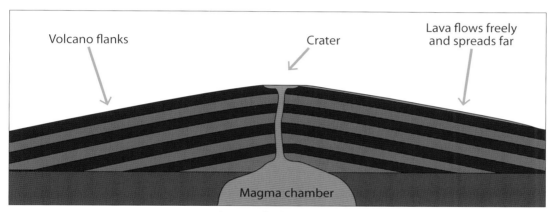

Features of a shield volcano

A shield volcano is cone-shaped with gently-sloping flanks (usually less than 10°). Its shape is formed by the runny (not viscous) lava it produces, which flows freely and spreads far. There is little gas in this type of eruption, so there is little explosive material. Mauna Kea in Hawaii, the Galapagos Islands, and Skjaldbreidur in Iceland are all examples of shield volcanoes.

Supervolcanoes

This term has been used since 2000 to describe a large volcano that is capable of causing a caldera-forming 'super eruption'. Supervolcanoes can be dangerous and their eruptions can have global consequences.

Formation of a supervolcano

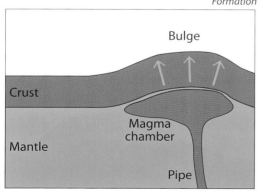

Before eruption

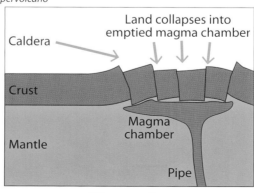

After eruption

Some of the largest volcanoes on Earth (such as Mauna Kea and Mauna Loa) are not considered 'supervolcanoes' because they can not produce a high-volume explosive eruption. To be classified as a supervolcano, a volcano must:

- produce at least 1000 km^3 of explosive material (a large volcano might only erupt 1 km^3).
- produce a caldera (when the land collapses into the empty magma chamber).
- have a ridge of higher land around it.
- erupt very infrequently – usually with hundreds of thousands of years between each eruption event.

The Toba eruption on the Indonesian island of Sumatra, estimated at 74,000 years ago, is the largest known eruption in history. Some scientists believe that humans were nearly wiped out by this supervolcano eruption. Around 2800 km^3 of ash was erupted and a caldera measuring 100 km by 40 km was left. The eruption also released 2000 million tonnes of sulphur dioxide, which could have blocked sunlight for several weeks and caused a global temperature fall of 3–5 degrees for at least a year.

The potential global impacts on people and the environment of a supervolcano eruption (e.g. Yellowstone)

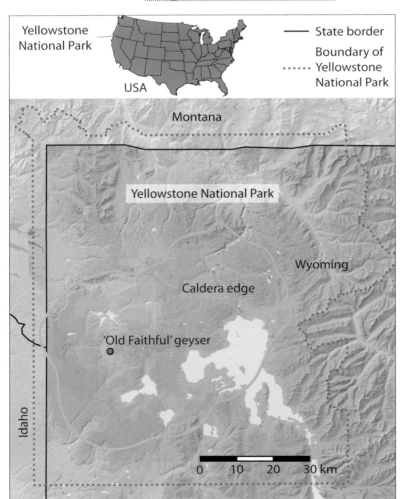

In Yellowstone National Park in Wyoming, USA there is a caldera capable of producing a super eruption. In recent years a number of small earthquakes have been recorded. For example, on the 30 March 2014, an earthquake occurred measuring 4.8 on the Richter scale. Geologists are also monitoring the movement of the Yellowstone plateau, which has been rising at a rate of 1.5 cm per year due to increased pressure in the magma chamber.

If a supervolcano eruption ever occurred at Yellowstone, it could bring about a global catastrophe.

Map of the Yellowstone caldera

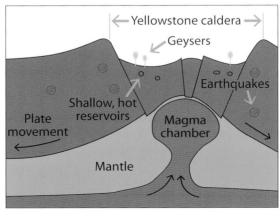

Cross section of the Yellowstone caldera

POTENTIAL IMPACTS ON PEOPLE	POTENTIAL IMPACTS ON THE ENVIRONMENT
Death and destruction – Over 90,000 people could be killed instantly in the USA due to the explosion and pyroclastic event.	**Ejecta** – a supervolcano could eject at least 1000 km³ (compared to 1 km³ of a normal volcano). This could include a 25-mile-high ash cloud.
Impact of the ash – Ash clouds would blow across the globe (reaching the UK in five days), blanketing soil, clogging machinery and causing respiratory and health problems for people. Lahars could devastate whole communities. The sulphur dioxide in the air could ensure that very little solar radiation would penetrate the sulphates in the upper atmosphere. The heat from the Sun would be directly reflected back into space – causing darkness and temperatures to drop dramatically. This could change ecosystems, which could make it difficult to grow food globally.	**Ash** – The ash thrown into the upper atmosphere could circulate around the globe and cause a 'dark summer', where no sunlight gets through for at least one year. 1000 miles away, the layer of ash deposited on the ground could be over three metres thick. Some of this could cause lahar flows (when water and ash mixes together and flows downhill as a thick mudslide). Global temperatures could drop by 3–5 degrees and remain low for many years. This could start a global mini ice age. Plants and animals could die due to the climate change and it would take hundreds of years for conditions to return to those pre-eruption.
Food security – In the USA and globally, crops and food supplies could suffer significantly, leading to increased food prices, famine and starvation. In turn, this could lead to civil unrest.	**Pyroclastic event** – Everything within a 100-mile radius of the eruption could be destroyed.
Changing a way of life – Homes could be destroyed; air, road and rail travel and transport could grind to a halt; and water supplies could be contaminated. Life as we know it could change radically and survival could become increasingly difficult.	**Ecosystem destruction** – Whole ecosystems could be destroyed. Crops could be destroyed due to ash fall and animals could die due to respiratory problems and starvation.
Long-term survival – If a global mini ice age was triggered due to the supervolcanic eruption, plants and animals would die quickly. People would have less access to food and water, and the human population would decrease rapidly. It could take hundreds of years for the ecosystems to return to normal.	

 Test your revision

1. Describe the main features of a composite volcano.
2. Describe the main characteristics of a shield volcano.
3. Describe the main characteristics of a supervolcano.
4. Describe the potential global impacts on people if a supervolcano were to erupt.

Practice Questions

Getting the best grade possible

There are three units that you must complete for your CCEA GCSE in Geography:

- **Unit 1: Understanding Our Natural World** (physical geography)
  1 hour 30 mins exam paper (40% of the overall GCSE qualification)
- **Unit 2: Living in Our World** (human geography)
  1 hour 30 mins exam paper (40% of the overall GCSE qualification)
- **Unit 3: Fieldwork**
  1 hour exam paper (20% of the overall GCSE qualification)

This student guide covers unit 1, so the following advice focuses on the Unit 1 exam paper. However, some of the guidance could also be applied to Units 2 and 3.

Exam advice

1. What to bring with you to the exam

Bring a ruler, a pencil, a black pen, a calculator, a protractor (angle measure) and a packet of five colouring pencils with you to the exam.

2. Manage your time

You have 90 minutes (1½ hours) to sit your Unit 1 exam paper. You need to manage your time well to make sure you get it completed.

The table opposite shows how the exam paper is structured, the marks for each question, and how long you should spend on it. You will see that there is a question for each chapter of the study material in this book.

Unit 1: Understanding Our Natural World

Question	Description	Marks (out of 100)	Exam timing (out of 90 minutes)
Q1: Theme A: River Environments	One multi-part question addressing rivers (might also include map work).	25	22½ minutes
Q2: Theme B: Coastal Environments	One multi-part question addressing coasts (might also include map work).	25	22½ minutes
Q3: Theme C: Our Changing Weather and Climate	One multi-part question addressing weather and climate.	25	22½ minutes
Q4: Theme D: The Restless Earth	One multi-part question addressing plate tectonics, basic rock types, earthquakes and volcanoes.	25	22½ minutes
Quality of Written Communication	The examiner will assess the quality of written communication of your answers to three questions on the paper.	Part of the marks allocation	Part of the time allocation

3. Use the marks as a guide

Each question (1, 2, 3 and 4) is broken down into smaller parts (a, b, c, etc.).
Use the marks allocated alongside each part to help you work out how long to spend on it and how much depth you need to go into for your answer. You need to work quickly through the shorter questions so that you have more time to spend on longer response questions.

- For a question worth 7 marks you should aim to spend around 7 minutes answering it. Don't spend any longer or you won't get the paper finished in time. Keep your answers concise and get straight to the point.
- The number of lines also provides a good indication of how much you should write.

4. Answer the question asked

It is important to read each question thoroughly to make sure that you know what you are being asked to do. One of the biggest mistakes that candidates make is not answering the question asked on the exam paper. Ideally, you should read every question **three** times. On the third reading it is a good idea to circle any command or key words. If you are asked to refer to a resource or a case study, make sure that you use specific facts and details that relate to the question.

5. Understand the command words

Make sure that you know what the common command words mean. There is a big difference between a question that asks you to **describe** a graph and one that asks you to **explain** the trend shown on a graph.

Compare	What are the main differences and similarities?
Contrast	What are the main differences?
Describe	Give details of a known concept or case study, or use details to show the shape or pattern of a resource. What does it look like? What are the highs, lows and averages?
Discuss	Describe and explain. Argue a particular point, but you might need to address both sides of an argument (agree and disagree).
Explain	Give reasons why a pattern or feature exists using geographical knowledge.
Evaluate	Look at the positive and negative points of a particular strategy or theory and give an overall concluding statement.
Identify	Choose or select.
Outline	Set out the main characteristics. Provide a brief description or explanation as required by the question.

6. Structure your answer

If an exam question seems daunting, try breaking it down into chunks. This will help you to structure the answer fully. For example, the following question could be asked in the Unit 1 exam:

"Evaluate the river management strategy used on a river outside the British Isles that you have studied." [7]

To answer this question, you must:

1. recognise that it is referring to:
   a) river management, and
   b) outside the British Isles (e.g. the Yangtse River, China).

2. evaluate the management strategy, which means:
   a) briefly describe the details of the river management strategy case study within the context of the river.
   b) look at the positive and negative features of this particular strategy.
   c) provide an overall concluding statement, which clearly shows whether the strategy was mostly positive or mostly negative.

   A 7-mark question will be marked using a levels of response mark scheme. Any evaluate answer should include a balanced look at both the positives and negatives of the strategy, followed by a concluding evaluative statement.

7. If you have time at the end

If you have some time left after completing the paper, then it is important that you check through your answers and make sure that you have:

a) answered everything, and

b) included as much detail as possible.

Use every second to squeeze every last mark out of your paper that you can.

 Revision tip

Your hand can be your most useful tool! Cover up your answers with your hand and ask yourself the question again. Think about what things you would expect in a good answer for this question and look under your hand to see what you wrote. Add in anything you missed.

Exam-style questions

The following pages provide exam-style questions and examples of student answers **in blue**. These student answers provide a basis for your own response and will be followed by some examiner tips **in red** to show how the answers could have been improved.

Theme A: River Environments

1. (a) Study **Figure 1** which shows a drainage basin. Answer the questions that follow.

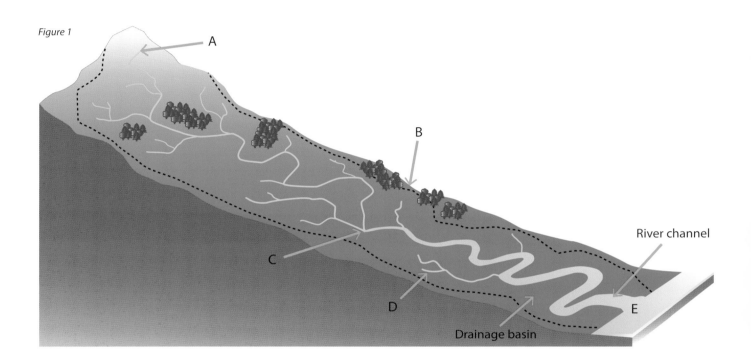

Figure 1

Key	
A =	Where the river begins.
B =	The area of high ground that separates one drainage basin from its neighbour.
C =	The place where two rivers join.
D =	A small, narrow river that will join with the main river.
E =	Where the river meets the sea.

(b) Complete the key for Fig 1 by labelling features A–E. [5]

Key	
A = source	Where the river begins.
B = watershed	The area of high ground that separates one drainage basin from its neighbour.
C = confluence	The place where two rivers join.
D = tributary	A small, narrow river that will join with the main river.
E = mouth	Where the river meets the sea.

5/5 marks awarded
This is a straightforward question. The student should be able to identify and label the parts of the drainage basin system easily. Each answer has been correctly identified. 1 mark for each correct answer.

(c) Name two transfers of water within the drainage basin system. [2]

   1. Groundwater
   2. Infiltration

1/2 marks awarded
The mark scheme for this question notes that there are 2 marks available. 1 mark for each correct transfer (surface runoff/overland flow, infiltration, throughflow, percolation or groundwater flow). The student is awarded 1 mark as only one transfer has been correctly identified. Groundwater is NOT correct as the answer needed to include 'flow' to show a movement through the system.

(d) State the meaning of the term **groundwater flow**. [2]

   Groundwater flow is when water is in the rock. If the soil has infiltrated too much water it becomes saturated.

1/2 marks awarded
The student has given a basic description of groundwater flow but the elaboration does not refer to groundwater. For example, a simple definition might be 'water moves slowly through the rocks and back into the sea'.

2. Study Figure 2 which shows how load size varies along the course of the Glenarm River in Co. Antrim. Answer the questions that follow.

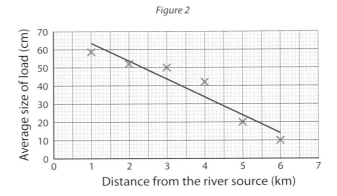

Figure 2

(a) Describe how load size changes along the Glenarm River. [4]

> When the load is closer to the source it is larger (cm). The size of the load at 1 km is 58 cm. As the load travels further downstream it becomes smaller in size. At 4 km from the river source the load is 42 cm and as it travels to 6 km the size is 10 cm.

3 /4 marks awarded
Longer questions are usually marked using levels of response:

Level 1 = 1 mark
A basic statement regarding the graph or bedload change in general.

Level 2 = 2–3 marks
A limited description that relates to the graph. For 2 marks the answer must contain at least one figure relating to size and for 3 marks there must be at least two figures on size.

Level 3 = 4 marks
A detailed description regarding trend, referring to at least two figures on size, and recognising that from 4 km the load size reduces faster than before.

This answer is awarded 3 marks based on the comments on stone size. However, it will not be awarded full marks as it does not mention the sudden drop in stone size at 5 km and 6 km.

(b) Identify the **two** types of erosion that explain the pattern shown in **Figure 2**. Choose and underline your answers from the list of river processes below.

Saltation   <u>**Abrasion**</u>   **Traction**   <u>**Attrition**</u>   **Suspension**   [2]

2/2 marks awarded: Abrasion and Attrition are the processes that are involved in eroding the load in a river. The other three are all transportation processes within the river. The student has underlined both correct answers.

3. Name one transportation process and describe how it carries material downstream. [3]

> Saltation is a transportation process that happens when some bits of rock in the river are bounced along.

2/3 marks awarded

The mark scheme for this question notes that there is 1 mark available for accurately naming one transportation process and another 2 marks are available for a valid response that explains the process.

This answer accurately names saltation (the alternatives are traction, suspension and solution) but the explanation is quite basic and needs a bit more depth. A better answer might explain that 'this process occurs only when heavier particles cannot be held up in the flow of the river all of the time' or that 'the stones are bounced along the riverbed'.

4. With reference to a river in the British Isles, explain the physical and human causes of a flood on your named river. [7]

> Name of river: Valency
>
> Causes of the flood:
>
> Physical – It had rained 12 out of 14 days that month. The day of the flood it rained 185 mm in 5 hours and this meant that the soil was saturated. Since the soil could no longer infiltrate, the water ran down the surface of the drainage basin.
>
> Human – The bridge's arch was very low so as the fast river flowed underneath, debris (e.g. trees) got trapped below the arch. This created a large blockage, which caused all of the surrounding land to get flooded with water.

6/7 marks awarded

The mark scheme for this question notes that if the student names a river outside the British Isles or does not name a river, a maximum of Level 1 will be awarded.

Level 1 = 1–2 marks
A basic response that may simply state a cause of flooding, e.g. heavy rain.

Level 2 = 3–5 marks
A limited explanation of the causes of flooding on a named river in the British Isles.

Level 3 = 6–7 marks
A detailed explanation of the causes of flooding for a named river in the British Isles.

The student has given facts to support the case study but lacks some detail. For example, the date (16 August) could be stated and the correct amount of rainfall was 200–300 mm. However, there still is some solid geographical explanation and the student has done well to balance both the physical and human factors within the answer.

Theme B: Coastal Environments

5. Coastlines are constantly shaped by waves.
State two facts about constructive waves. [2]

> Constructive waves have a strong wash and a weak backwash. Constructive waves build up the beach as they bring sediment up the beach.

2/2 marks awarded
There is 1 mark for each correct fact related to constructive waves. The student has identified two separate facts, so maximum marks can be awarded.

6. Study **Figure 3** which shows a photograph of a coastal spit at Spurn Head in Yorkshire. Answer the questions that follow.

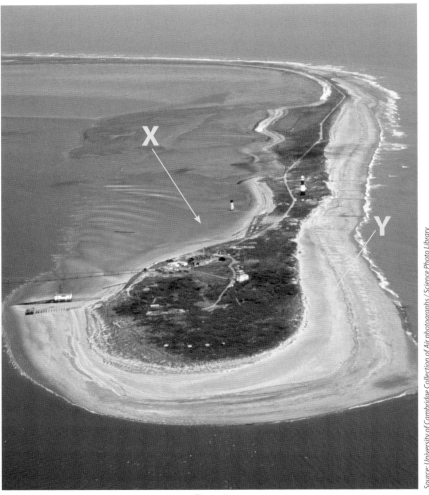

Source: University of Cambridge Collection of Air photographs / Science Photo Library

Figure 3

(a) Identify the two features labelled **X** and **Y**. Choose your answers from the list below.

Salt marsh   Deposited sand and shingle   Longshore drift   Prevailing wind [2]

> X = Salt marsh
> Y = Longshore drift

1/2 marks awarded
There is 1 mark for correctly identifying each of the two features. X is salt marsh and Y is the location of the deposited sand and shingle. The student correctly identified X but not Y.

(b) Explain the formation of a spit.   [6]

> Eroded material from the coast is transported by longshore drift. Prevailing winds cause the waves to change direction. The eroded material is transported by longshore drift and is now deposited where the coastline changes direction, which allows the spit to form as constant deposition occurs. Prevailing winds cause the spit to hook and the water behind this spit becomes still and turns into marshland. Spits take hundreds of years to form.

3/6 marks awarded
The mark scheme for this question notes:

Level 1 = 1–2 marks
The answer makes basic reference to the movement of sand.

Level 2 = 3–4 marks
A limited explanation that refers to either the conditions required for a spit to develop or the process involved.

Level 3 = 5–6 marks
A detailed explanation is provided for both the conditions required for a spit to develop and the processes involved.

The student has attempted to write about both the processes and conditions but does not include enough detail to support the answer. There is not enough depth for this to be a Level 3 answer. A low Level 2 mark was awarded because the processes were not fully developed. It is important that students can clearly understand and explain a sequence of events in relation to spit formation.

7. Explain the formation of a stack. [6]

At any cliff face where the sea and land meet, cracks can start to develop in any weakness found in the rocks. These cracks are usually caused by attrition, as the sea attacks the rock on a regular basis. The cracks will eventually form into caves. The erosion will continue in the cave (mostly through abrasion) and the cave might be eroded enough to form an arch. Waves will continue to erode and the weight of the rock in the arch will become so heavy that the roof of the arch will collapse to form a stack.

5/6 marks awarded
The mark scheme for this question notes:

Level 1 = 1–2 marks
A basic correct statement about stack formation.

Level 2 = 3–4 marks
A limited explanation relating to stack formation.

Level 3 = 5–6 marks
A detailed explanation of how stacks are formed, noting the process of erosion and the development of the features from crack, cave, arch to stack.

The student has answered the question well. There is some discussion of the role that erosion plays in the process and a clear understanding of the steps leading up to the development of a stack.

8. With reference to a case study from the British Isles, evaluate the sustainability of a coastal management strategy you have studied. [9]

Newcastle (Co. Down): Sea wall

Newcastle had a storm that ruined its initial sea wall. The sea wall that can be seen today reflects and absorbs some of the wave energy. It has a deep foundation that prevents erosion on the sea bed. The sea wall protects shops, tourist attractions and residential homes. It cost at least £10 million. It is a large concrete wall that surrounds the entire coast of Newcastle. Some people say it is an eyesore and some say it has ruined the natural beauty of the area. It needs constant maintenance in order to make it effective.

5/9 marks awarded
The mark scheme for this question notes:

Level 1 = 1–3 marks
A basic description or evaluation of coastal management which may not name a location.

Level 2 = 4–6 marks
A limited description of a coastal management strategy with a basic evaluation.

Level 3 = 7–9 marks
A detailed description and evaluation of the sustainability of one coastal management strategy. Answers should include relevant case study detail to support the answer.

This answer contains some good detail in relation to the sea wall in Newcastle but needs to go further. Balance is needed between the positive and negative aspects of the strategy and its sustainability. The answer also needs to include some form of final statement about the sustainability of this particular approach.

Theme C: Our Changing Weather and Climate

9. Study **Figure 4** which shows a weather forecast for an anticyclone over Northern Ireland in July. Answer the questions that follow.

Figure 4

> A. The temperature will be a very warm 28 °C.
> B. The wind speed will be calm.
> C. Warm air will come from a south-easterly direction.
> D. There will be no rain.

(a) Complete **Table 1** by adding the names of the instruments that could be used to collect information on each of the weather elements in the forecast in **Figure 4**.   [4]

Table 1

Weather element	Instrument
A	
B	
C	
D	

Weather element	Instrument
A	Thermometer
B	Anemometer
C	Wind vane
D	Rain gauge

4/4 marks awarded
The student has successfully identified each of the four pieces of equipment that are used to measure the elements of the weather.

(b) State the name of the air mass that could have brought this weather [1]

   Tropical maritime

0/1 marks awarded
The most likely air mass to bring this type of weather is tropical continental, as it brings warm and dry weather.

(c) Explain why there will be no rain. [3]

   Anticyclones rarely bring rain as they are high pressure. Also tropical maritime air masses bring very small amounts of rain or none at all, as they come from the south east. Also, the air mass will be going over France so it won't pick up any water on the way.

1/3 marks awarded:
The mark scheme for this question notes:

Award 1 mark
For a basic statement relating to the lack of rainfall.

Award 2 marks
For a limited statement relating to the lack of rainfall.

Award 3 marks
For an answer that has a detailed explanation relating to the lack of rainfall. For example, there are few clouds in the sky as the area experiences high pressure and is sinking. As the air sinks it will become warmer. This means that condensation does not happen and clouds cannot develop.

This student has continued to discuss the tropical maritime air mass from the question before but does include commentary of some value in the last sentence. More elaboration is needed to gain more marks.

10. Weather forecasts are created by the Met Office in the UK. They use satellite images to help build a forecast.

   Name the type of satellite that passes around the Earth from pole to pole. [1]

   Polar orbiting

1/1 mark awarded
The student has correctly identified this type of satellite. An alternative answer is polar.

11. Describe and explain how latitude can affect the climate of a place. [4]

   Latitude is the distance that you are from the equator. The closer you are to the equator, the warmer the temperature will be. Countries in Africa like Kenya will have warm temperatures but countries like the UK that are far from the equator will be much colder.

2/4 marks awarded
The mark scheme for this question notes:

Level 1 = 1 mark
A basic statement of how latitude might impact climate.

Level 2 = 2/3 marks
A limited description that deals with the main ways that latitude can impact the climate of an area. Will also include some explanation.

Level 3 = 4 marks
A detailed response that contains a description, an explanation and reference to facts/places to support the answer.

The student has correctly described how latitude might impact a place and has given some context. However, there is very little explanation of how this will affect the climate of the place.

12. Describe the difference between weather and climate. [4]

> Weather is the day-to-day condition of the atmosphere and the air that surrounds us but climate is the average weather conditions (sunshine, rainfall and temperature) that are noted over 35 years in a place. Weather is what is happening right now but climate is more long term.

4/4 marks awarded
The mark scheme for this question notes:

Level 1 = 1 mark
A basic answer that defines either weather or climate.

Level 2 = 2–3 marks
A limited answer that defines both weather and climate.

Level 3 = 4 marks
A detailed response that clearly distinguishes the differences between weather and climate.

The student has correctly described the definitions of the two key words and has also made sure to highlight the main differences between them.

13. Describe the impact that an extreme weather event outside the British Isles has had on people and on property. [8]

> One extreme weather event that we studied was hurricanes. Hurricane Katrina took place on 29 August 2005 in the USA. Over 1200 people died and 500,000 people were left homeless. There was no electricity for a long period of time. People had to move away and did not come back to their homes. Over 200,000 people lost their jobs and there was a lot of pollution in the local area.

4/8 marks awarded
The mark scheme for this question notes:

Level 1 = 1–2 marks
An answer that provides a basic description of the impact of a relevant weather event.

Level 2 = 3–5 marks
An answer that has a limited description of both the impact of the extreme weather event on people and property or an answer that deals with only one of the two impacts in some depth.

Level 3 = 6–8 marks
An answer that describes the impact of the extreme weather event on both people and property in some depth with good elaboration of factual detail.

This answer contains some good case study facts and figures. It addresses the impact on people but does not really deal with the impact on property. The student needs to make sure that both aspects of the answer are fully covered for maximum marks.

Theme D: The Restless Earth

14. Study **Table 2** which shows some types of rock. Answer the questions that follow.

Table 2

Name of rock	Rock type
Granite	
Limestone	
Slate	Metamorphic

(a) Complete Table 2 by identifying the rock type of each rock.
One has been completed for you. [2]

Name of rock	Rock type
Granite	Igneous
Limestone	Sedimentary
Slate	Metamorphic

2/2 marks awarded
The student has correctly identified the two additional rock types. 1 mark for each
correct answer.

(b) Explain how basalt is formed. [3]

Basalt is formed due to a volcano. The volcano erupts and lava
spreads over the land. Basalt cools fairly quickly on the surface and
this means it has little evidence of a crystalline structure.

3/3 marks awarded
The mark scheme for this question notes:

Award 1 mark
For a basic statement relating to basalt.

Award 2 marks
For a limited explanation relating to the formation of basalt.

Award 3 marks
For a detailed explanation that refers to cooling and small crystals forming.

The student has provided a good answer that explains and elaborates the formation of
basalt from a volcano. Maximum marks can be awarded.

15. Study **Figure 5** which shows part of the Earth's structure. Answer the questions that follow.

Figure 5

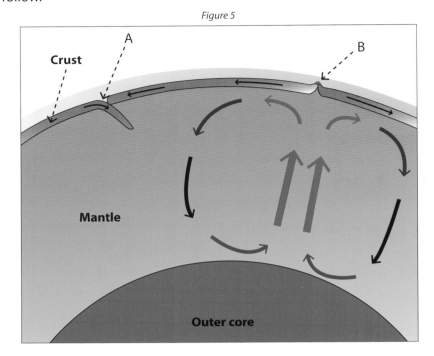

(a) Name the features **A and B**.

A _____

B _____ [2]

       A: Crust
       B: Volcano

1/2 marks awarded
The answer to A is either ocean trench or subduction zone. The answer to B is mid-ocean ridge or volcano.

The student has answered A incorrectly but B is correct.

(b) Use **Figure 5** to help you to explain why plates move. [3]

       Convection currents move in the mantle, as extreme heat from the Earth's core heats the rock in the mantle. This rock becomes less dense and causes it to rise to the surface and come back down as it cools. This then causes the plates to move.

2/3 marks awarded
The mark scheme for this question notes:

Award 1 mark
For a basic statement relating to plate movement.

Award 2 marks
For a limited explanation referring to convection currents.

Award 3 marks
For a detailed explanation that refers to plates being moved.

The student has made a good attempt to answer the question but a more detailed explanation is needed for maximum marks.

16 (a) Complete **Figure 6** by drawing arrows to show the direction of the plate movement and mark the likely place where most earthquakes would originate with an X. [2]

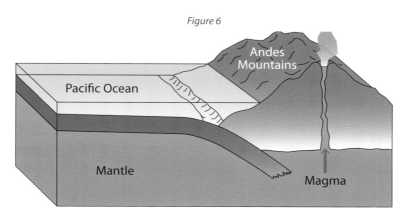

Figure 6

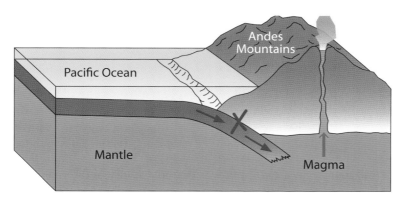

2/2 marks awarded
The student has put the arrows in the correct place and has identified that earthquakes can take place within the subduction zone where the two plates meet. Maximum marks are awarded.

(b) Name this type of plate boundary [1]

Destructive plate boundary

1/1 mark awarded
The correct plate boundary was identified as the destructive plate margin. Another acceptable answer is converging.

17. State the meaning of the term **liquefaction**.   [2]

> Liquefaction is when an earthquake causes buildings to sink into the ground.

1/2 marks awarded
Award 1 mark for a basic statement.

Award 2 marks for a full definition that refers to earthquakes as the cause.
For example, liquefaction occurs when an earthquake hits an area and shakes the wet soil. The shaking causes the water within the soil to start to rise to the surface, and this process turns solid soil and rock into a liquid mud.

The student has given a basic statement but the answer requires more elaboration on how liquefaction takes place to get the second mark.

18. Explain the causes of an earthquake in a MEDC or LEDC that you have studied.   [3]

> Name of earthquake: Great Tohoku Earthquake, Japan, 2011
>
> Japan lies on a destructive plate margin where the Philippine and Pacific Plates meet. The Pacific Plate has been moving in towards the Philippine Plate.

2/3 marks awarded
The mark scheme for this question notes:

Award 1 mark
For an answer that has a basic statement referring to plate movement. A maximum of 1 mark is awarded if there is no named earthquake or the earthquake is located in an MEDC.

Award 2 marks
For an answer that has a limited explanation referring to how plates move and the friction or stress that is built up.

Award 3 marks
For an answer that has a detailed explanation that refers to how plates move and friction or stress was built up to create an earthquake. There must be at least one fact that relates to the named earthquake.

The student has included some good facts and detail on the plates and the type of movement. For full marks the answer needed more elaboration on how the movement brought about the release of pressure that led to an earthquake. Candidates often fail to explain the simple cause of an earthquake before explaining the more complicated processes.

19. With reference to an earthquake that you have studied, describe the short- and long-term impacts on people after the event. [7]

Name of earthquake: Great Tohoku Earthquake, Japan, 2011

The Great Tohoku Earthquake took place in Japan on 11th March 2011 at 2.48 p.m. The earthquake caused many different problems for the people of Japan. It created over 300,000 refugees and people found it difficult to get even the most basic things like food, water and shelter. The weather was very cold and people struggled with the weather and climate. Another impact was that new tsunami barriers had to be built, which would stretch 18 m high, as the tsunami waves had been much bigger than expected.

4/7 marks awarded
The mark scheme for this question notes:

Level 1 = 1–2 marks
An answer that provides a basic description of the short- and long-term impacts.

Level 2 = 3–5 marks
An answer that provides a limited description of the short- and long-term impacts that fit within the parameters of the case study.

Level 3 = 6–7 marks
An answer that provides a detailed explanation of the short- and long-term impacts with a full discussion that provides good detail of the impacts of this particular case study.

This student has developed some good depth in relation to the short-term impact of the earthquake on people but could have further developed the long-term impacts with a little more detail. The comment about the tsunami barrier is not relevant to this particular question. Candidates need to make sure that they read the question carefully and respond accordingly.

Revision advice

The secret ingredient to successful revision is that you must LEARN your topics. Revision can be boring and it can be difficult to stay focused. However, you have to train your brain to learn things in the depth that you need. Here are some useful tips that can help you:

1. Start your revision early and plan it carefully so that you have enough time to cover the whole subject at least three times before the exam season starts.

2. Revision is not just reading; it involves taking notes and processing information.

3. You can't do that much revision sitting at your computer. Technology provides lots of amazing new ways to support your revision but try not to become distracted by the games, the drawings and the timetables. You may need to turn off your computer, tablet or phone, or leave your devices in another room to avoid distraction.

4. Some people like to revise in short bursts (e.g. 50 minutes), with mini breaks (e.g. 10 minutes) in between to have a cup of coffee, check their phone or go for a walk. Others like to revise for longer periods and set themselves a target (e.g. 3 hours), which they aim to meet, followed by a reward such as watching a TV programme. It doesn't matter how you organise yourself – all that matters is that you put the time and effort in.

5. Remember, just because you are sitting at the desk in your bedroom doesn't mean that you are actually achieving anything. Don't fool yourself; if you don't get the work done, you won't get the marks you want. If you are struggling to focus, ask your friends and parents to check on you more often to help keep you on task.

Understanding the way that YOU learn is very important. It is unlikely that you will be able to learn and remember things in the same way that your friends do. How much revision you need to do is a very individual thing.

Revision and learning techniques

There are many different revision and learning techniques. Everyone is different, so it can be useful to practise a variety of techniques until you find the one that works best for you.

1. Condense 3

This is a traditional technique that works well if you find it difficult to remember things over a long period of time. The aim is to create a set of 'trigger' words that will help to prompt knowledge in the middle of the exam.

> **Step 1:** Go through a particular topic and make notes about what you need to remember.
>
> **Step 2:** Now go through the notes you have made and try to condense them again onto an A5 page (one side).

Step 3: Condense the information for a third time by taking note of the key words on your A5 page and writing them on one A3 page. Your aim is to have one big page for each major topic, packed with the key 'trigger' words that you need to remember.

Step 4: Sit and learn the trigger words. Take each word in turn and say it aloud. Put your finger on the word on the page and think about what other information this trigger word leads you to.

2. Mind maps

This technique allows you to see the 'big picture' and is great for organising information. It can also be useful when trying to work out how to answer a question. Using the example below as a template, try to draw your own mind map for each topic and use them to answer practice questions.

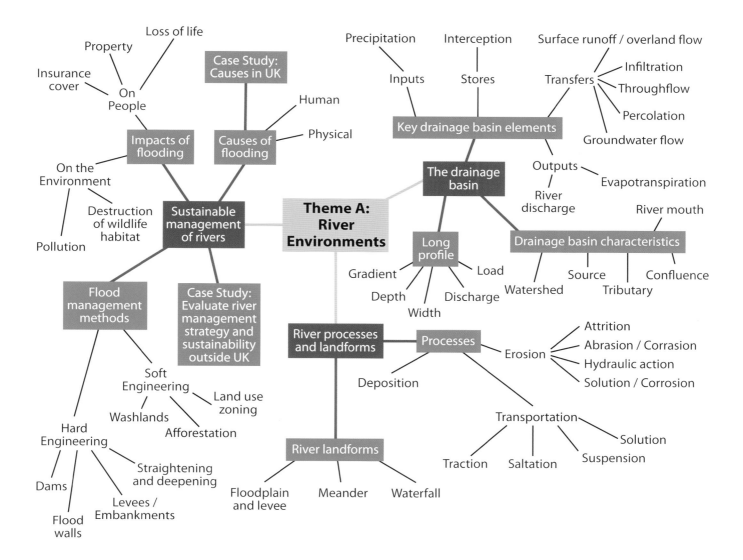

3. Traffic lighting

This technique offers a simple way for you to identify:

- what you already know
- what you nearly know
- what you do not know

You can use highlighters or coloured dots as you go through your notebook to indicate how well you know and understand various parts of the course.

4. Revision cards

You might find it useful to make your own revision cards to memorise. Here are two ways to organise them:

- Make one card for each topic or case study. Pack the card with information and key facts that will help support an answer. You could even have advantages on one side and disadvantages on the other.
- You could create your own Geography 'Top Trumps' type game, where you have key facts and features on a card and you have to remember where the case study place is.

5. Make your own podcast

Although there are some very good podcasts available that may help your revision, if you make your own, you can tailor it to your own needs. There is a lot of free software online that allows you to record your own MP3, so you can sit on the bus or go to bed listening to the facts and figures from your Geography course.

Some final advice about revising Geography...

Practise your case studies

Case studies are an important part of your GCSE Geography course. You will read a lot of background information that you won't be asked about in an examination but is needed for the case study to make sense. Make sure that you learn **only what you need to know** for each case study. Learn the location, the key facts and the main points that are raised about what the case study shows.

Practise questions involving case studies as much as you can. They make up a sizeable amount of the questions in your examination paper.

Glossary

River environments

Abrasion/corrasion: A process of erosion where the force of moving water grinds the stones being carried by the river against the riverbed and banks, and this dislodges material.

Afforestation: When trees are planted to intercept rainfall and help to lower the discharge in the river.

Attrition: A process of erosion where stones carried downstream knock against each other and start to wear each other down. This makes the load smaller and more rounded downstream.

Confluence: Where two rivers meet.

Dam: A wall built across a river channel to stop the river from moving downstream, controlling the amount of water that can travel through the river system.

Deposition: When the river load becomes too heavy for the river to carry and material is dumped (or deposited) along the river course.

Depth: How deep the water in a river is (usually measured in centimetres).

Discharge: The amount of water that passes a point in a river at a particular time (measured in cumecs – cubic metres of water per second).

Drainage basin: The area of land that is drained by a river and its tributaries.

Embankment: An artificial bank of material (earth or rock) that can raise/strengthen the sides of a river.

Erosion: When parts of the riverbank or riverbed are worn away. There are four main types of erosion: attrition, hydraulic action, abrasion/corrasion and solution/corrosion.

Evapotranspiration: Water is transferred from land and water surfaces to the atmosphere by evaporation and plant transpiration.

Flood wall: A wall built alongside a river to prevent water from reaching the floodplain.

Flooding: A temporary covering by water of land that is usually dry.

Floodplain: An area of land next to a river that is likely to flood. Silt is deposited when floodwater covers the area.

Gradient: The angle of the land.

Groundwater flow: Water moves slowly through the rock back into the sea.

Hard engineering methods: When a river undergoes major changes (e.g. building new flood walls) to try and prevent it from flooding. This type of management is not usually sustainable in the long term.

Hydraulic action: A process of erosion where the speed and force of the water removes material from the riverbed and banks.

Infiltration: Water soaks (filters) into the soil.

Interception: When water is trapped by vegetation (store) before it reaches the ground.

Land use zoning: A planning measure where land within a floodplain is divided up into areas that experience different degrees of flood risk.

Levee: A build-up of material on the banks of a river caused by repeated flooding. It raises the height of the riverbank. The largest, coarsest material will be dumped close to the riverbank.

Levee (artificial): A man-made ridge built from rocks and sand alongside a riverbank to protect the floodplain from flooding.

Load: The material that the river is carrying.

Meander: A bend in a river. The river flows fastest on the outside of the bend, causing erosion. The river flows slower on the inside of the bend, causing deposition.

Percolation: Water moves from the soil into the spaces (pores) in the rock.

Precipitation: Water vapour condenses into drizzle, rain, sleet, snow and hail, and this falls towards the surface of the land.

River cliff: The outside of a meander, where the fast-flowing water causes erosion of the riverbank, creating a steep bank.

River landforms: The main features that can be found along the course of a river. They are usually formed by either erosion or deposition in the river.

River management strategy: A plan used to reduce the likelihood of flooding and damage due to flooding.

River mouth: The place where the river flows into the sea.

Saltation: A process of transportation where some of the heavier particles of eroded material are bounced along the riverbed but are not held up in the flow of the river.

Slip-off slope: The inside of a meander, where river load is deposited because of the slower flow of water.

Soft engineering methods: Methods that manage the river (e.g. afforestation) rather than prevent the river from flooding. This type of management does not damage the river and is usually more sustainable than hard engineering methods.

Solution/corrosion (erosion): A process of erosion where weak acid (chemicals) in the water reacts with the rock and dissolves soluble materials.

Solution (transportation): A process of transportation where some minerals dissolve easily in water and microscopic particles are held up in the solution of the water.

Source: The starting point of a river.

Straightening and deepening the river: When a river channel is straightened, widened or deepened to help it carry the water downstream more efficiently.

Surface runoff/overland flow: Water moves across the surface of the land.

Suspension: A process of transportation where the water speed increases and the river picks up particles. The particles are carried along in the flow of the water and do not make contact with the riverbed.

Throughflow: Water moves downhill through the soil.

Traction: A process of transportation where the heaviest particles of eroded material in the river are rolled along the riverbed.

Transportation: When eroded material is carried from one place to another through a river system. There are four main types of transportation: traction, saltation, suspension and solution.

Tributary: A small river or stream that flows into a larger river.

Washlands: An area of land that acts as a storage area for river water to 'wash' into during a flood. It is usually found in the lower course of a river.

Water cycle: A natural system where water is in constant movement above, on or below the surface of the Earth, and is changing state from water vapour (gas) to liquid and into ice (solid).

Waterfall: A waterfall forms where water flows from an area of hard rock to an area of softer rock. The softer rock underneath is eroded away causing the cliff edge to gradually move backwards.

Watershed: The dividing line between one drainage basin and another.

Width: The measurement of the distance from one river bank to the other river bank (usually measured in m).

Theme B
Coastal Environments

Abrasion/corrasion: A process of erosion where the force of moving water grinds the stones being carried by the sea against the cliffs and rocks (acting like sandpaper). This dislodges material.

Arch: An opening in a headland caused by waves eroding the rock in a cave until it cuts the whole way through.

Attrition: A process of erosion where stones and boulders that are being carried by the sea knock together and start to wear each other down. This knocks the edges off the stones and results in smaller and rounder stones.

Beach: A gentle, sloping area of land that is built up by constructive waves moving deposited material (sand, shingle and pebbles) up the slope.

Beach nourishment: When sand or pebbles are added artificially to a beach to replenish or build it up.

Cave: An opening in a cliff caused by erosion from water widening any weaknesses or cracks in the rock.

Cliff: A high, steep rock face that is caused by coastal erosion.

Coastal defences: A range of measures that are used to protect the coast from flooding and erosion.

Coastal landforms: The features formed by either erosion or deposition by the sea.

Coastal management strategy: A plan that aims to reduce the likelihood of coastal flooding and erosion, and limit the damage that they can cause.

Constructive waves: Waves that surge up the beach. They help to build it up; are flat, gentle and shallow (around 1 m high); and break at a rate of only a few waves per minute (between six and nine).

Deposition: When waves lose energy, they dump (deposit) the material they were carrying.

Destructive waves: Waves that break on a steeply-sloping beach. They help to erode the beach; are steep (up to 5–6 m high) and close together; and break at a rate of around 15 waves per minute.

Erosion: When parts of the land or beaches are worn away. There are four main types of erosion: abrasion/corrasion, attrition, solution/corrosion and hydraulic action.

Gabions: Metal cages that are filled with rocks. These are stacked together to create a rock wall that will absorb wave energy.

Groynes: Wooden, concrete or rock barriers that are built at 90 degrees to the coastline. They trap the sand carried along the shore by longshore drift.

Hard engineering methods: When a coastline undergoes major changes (e.g. building sea walls) to try and prevent erosion and flooding. This type of management is not usually sustainable in the long term.

Headland: A stretch of the coast made of rock that sticks out into the sea. It occurs in areas containing both hard and soft rock. Waves erode the softer rock away and the harder, more resistant rock is left behind.

Hooked spit: A narrow ridge of land that becomes hooked in shape due to the action of wind and waves. This usually occurs where there is a change of direction along the coastline.

Hydraulic action: An erosion process where the force of the water pounds against the cliffs and dislodges material.

Longshore drift: A transportation process where eroded material is carried along the beach in a zig-zag course.

Managed retreat: Coastal land management used to allow erosion and flooding to occur on marginal land (so that more valuable land can be protected).

Sandy beach: A beach made up of very small material. Surging waves move coarser material up the beach, while finer material remains close to the water.

Sea walls: Solid walls that are used to separate the land from the sea. Often these are shaped to reflect wave energy back into the sea.

Shingle beach: A beach made up of large material. During stormy conditions, the waves throw shingle high up the beach which can form into ridges.

Soft engineering methods: Methods that manage the coastline (e.g. beach nourishment) rather than prevent erosion and flooding. This type of management does not damage the coastline and is usually more sustainable that hard engineering methods.

Solution/corrosion: A process of erosion where salts and acids in the seawater slowly dissolve coastal cliffs.

Spit: A long, narrow ridge of land that is made up of deposited (sand and shingle) material along a coastline. This usually occurs where there is a change of direction along the coastline.

Stack: A column of rock close to the coast. It is created when an arch is eroded away until its roof falls into the sea.

Transportation: When eroded material in the sea is moved from one place to another by the water. This uses the same four methods as rivers (traction, saltation, suspension and solution) but most material is carried along the coast by a process called longshore drift.

Wave cut platform: A gently-sloping, sometimes flat area produced by cliff retreat, as a result of erosional processes.

Wave: The movement of water as the wind blows across the surface of the sea. The size of any wave depends on its fetch (distance that the wave travels in open water).

Theme C — Our Changing Weather and Climate

Air mass: A body of air with similar temperature and moisture characteristics, which is often thousands of kilometres wide.

Altitude: The height above sea level.

Anemometer: A device used to measure wind speed in knots.

Anticyclone: An area of high pressure that produces calm, settled weather with little cloud cover or precipitation.

Atmospheric pressure: The pressure applied to the Earth's surface by the weight of the atmosphere.

Barometer: A device used to measure the atmospheric pressure of a place in millibars.

Buoys: A weather station moored in the ocean that records weather information and sends it back to weather centres.

Cirrus: Very high wispy clouds that are usually made up of ice particles.

Climate: The average weather taken over a long period of time (usually over 35 years). It is a less dynamic process than weather and does not change as quickly.

Cloud cover: The amount of sky covered by cloud. It is recorded as eighths (or oktas) of the sky covered.

Cloud types: A cloud is a visible mass of tiny water droplets floating in the atmosphere. It consists of water formed from the condensation of water vapour. Clouds are split into categories based on their shape and height.

Cold front: The boundary between an advancing cold air mass and a warm air mass. It brings a change in weather and a narrow belt of rain and clouds.

Cumulonimbus: Towering clouds that bring moisture. They start to tower as air rises and can bring hail, thunder and lightning.

Cumulus: Clouds that seem to move fast. They are white, have a fluffy appearance and can bring rain.

Digital thermometer: A digital device used to measure the temperature of the air in degrees centigrade.

Frontal depression: An area of low atmospheric pressure that produces cloudy, rainy and windy weather.

Geostationary satellite: A small spacecraft that hovers over the same spot on the Earth, moving at the speed of the Earth's rotation, and records the weather.

Knots: The unit of measurement for wind speed. One knot is roughly equivalent to one mile per hour.

Land-based station: An observation station that measures various elements of the weather.

Latitude: The position north or south of the equator. Generally, the greater the distance from the equator, the colder the climate will be.

Millibars: The unit of measurement for atmospheric pressure.

Okta: The unit of measurement for cloud cover. Each okta makes up one eighth of the sky.

Polar continental: An air mass that originates over Eastern Europe and Russia. It is more common in winter than summer in the British Isles.

Polar maritime: An air mass that originates in the north-Atlantic ocean. It is a common air mass in the British Isles.

Polar satellite: A small spacecraft that travels around the Earth from pole to pole and records the weather.

Precipitation: The form of moisture in the atmosphere (e.g. water, dew, hail, rain, sleet and snow). The amount of precipitation is measured in millimetres.

Prevailing wind: The most common wind direction for a location.

Rain gauge: A device used to measure the amount of rain that falls in a given area in a 24-hour period.

Rainfall radar: A type of pulse-Doppler radar is used to locate the amount of precipitation in the atmosphere.

Satellite image: An image of Earth captured from space.

Stratus: Layered clouds that are usually quite low in the sky. They are flat, featureless and often grey in colour, and bring light drizzle or small amounts of snow.

Synoptic chart: A weather map that gives a snapshot of the weather across a region. It summarises a large amount of complicated, detailed information.

Temperature: A measure of the amount of heat in the atmosphere.

Tropical continental: An air mass that originates in north Africa. It is the least common air mass affecting the British Isles.

Tropical maritime: An air mass that originates in the mid-Atlantic ocean and moves over the south west of the British Isles.

Warm front: The boundary between an advancing warm air mass and a cold air mass. It brings a belt of cloud and some rain. The rain will gradually increase as the front gets closer.

Warm sector: An area of relative calm and clear skies before a cold front passes and brings rain. Is part of a depression.

Weather: The day-to-day state of the atmosphere. It is a dynamic process that is constantly changing. The elements of the weather include temperature, precipitation, wind direction and speed, atmospheric pressure, cloud type and cloud cover.

Weather forecast: A prediction of how the weather is likely to change over the next few days and how this will affect people (e.g. what clothes to wear).

Wind direction: The direction that the wind is blowing from.

Wind speed: A measurement of how fast the air moves. It is usually measured in knots or kilometres per hour.

Wind vane: A device used to observe the direction that the wind is blowing from.

Theme D

The Restless Earth

Collision zone: A boundary where two continental crust plates move towards each other. The plates push each other upwards. This causes fold mountains and earthquakes.

Composite volcano: A cone-shaped volcano, with quite steep sides (usually between 30° and 40°), made up of alternating layers of hardened ash and lava.

Conservative plate margin: A boundary where two plates slip past each other. They either move in different directions or move in the same direction but at different rates. This causes earthquakes.

Constructive plate margin: A boundary where two plates move away from each other. New crust is created in the gap and this movement causes undersea volcanoes and earthquakes.

Convection current: The movement of molten mantle caused by heat and pressure from deep inside the Earth. This moves the hard crust above it.

Crust: The thin layer in the outermost section of the Earth. It ranges from 5–70 km in thickness. It is broken up into several large sections known as plates.

Destructive plate margin: A boundary where two different types of plate move towards each other. The denser oceanic crust plate moves towards the lighter but thicker continental crust plate and the oceanic plate is forced underneath. This causes volcanoes, earthquakes and ocean trenches.

Earthquake: A shaking of the Earth's crust due to the movement of the Earth's plates.

Epicentre: The point on the Earth's surface directly above the focus of an earthquake. It is where the shock waves are first felt at the surface.

Fault line: A crack in the Earth's surface where two plates slip past each other. Friction builds up over time and can cause earthquakes when it is released.

Focus: The place where an earthquake originally occurs deep inside the crust.

Fold mountain: Mountains created when two continental plates are forced together and pushed (folded) upwards.

Igneous rock: Rocks formed when molten rock (magma/lava) from underneath the Earth's crust cools and hardens. Examples include basalt and granite.

Inner core: The layer at the centre of the Earth. It is around 2200 km thick, temperatures are over 6000°C and the material there is much denser than material at the crust.

Liquefaction: The process of wet soil turning into liquid mud. It occurs when the shaking caused by an earthquake makes the water within wet soil rise to the surface.

Mantle: The thickest layer of the Earth (at 2900 km). It is made up of silicate rocks that remain molten and can move about.

Metamorphic rock: Rocks that have changed from an earlier state through the addition of pressure or heat. Examples include slate and marble.

Mid-ocean ridge: A landform created at constructive plate margins where two plates move away from each other and create a gap in the seabed. This gap is filled with fresh magma material from deep within the Earth.

Ocean trench: A deep ocean trench where two plates meet. It is caused by an oceanic plate being forced under a continental plate.

Outer core: The liquid layer that surrounds the inner core. The outer core is 1200 km thick.

Plate margin/boundary: The place where two plates meet. The boundaries include constructive, destructive and conservative plate margins, and collision zone.

Richter scale: A scale used to measure the strength of an earthquake.

Rock type: Rock is a solid, natural mass of mineral material that makes up the crust of the Earth. There are three types of rocks: igneous, sedimentary and metamorphic.

Sedimentary rock: Rocks formed by sediment that has built up over a long period of time, usually under water. Examples include limestone and sandstone.

Seismograph: An instrument used to measure the intensity of seismic waves (energy) during an earthquake. A weight with a pen attached, suspended from a spring, records measurements on a rotating drum.

Shield volcano: A cone-shaped volcano, with gently-sloping flanks (usually less than 10°), made up of runny lava flows that harden on top of each other.

Subduction zone: An area where oceanic plate is pushed underneath continental plate at a destructive plate margin. The friction created can cause earthquakes.

Supervolcano: A large volcano that is capable of causing a caldera-forming 'super eruption'. It has the potential of erupting at least 1000 km^3 of material that could have global consequences.

Tectonic plate: A large section of the Earth's crust. The crust is divided into many sections or plates, which move about on top of the mantle. There are two types of plate: continental and oceanic.

Tsunami: A large wave that is created when an underwater earthquake sends shockwaves through the water.

Volcano: Where lava, ash and gas erupts through a vent in the crust.

Copyright

Credits

Where information or data has been used, sources are cited within the body of the book.

The following photographs are included with the kind permission of the copyright holders. The numbers denote page numbers:

Cover image: iStock photo

Crown copyright: 16

iStock photo: 32 (bottom), 49, 50 (bottom), 52 (both), 90

Tim Manson: 2 (top), 13 (bottom two), 28 (both), 33, 58 (all), 82 (all), 83 (all)

University of Cambridge Collection of Air photographs / Science Photo Library: 76

U.S. Army Corps of Engineers photo by Cameron Siegal: 32

USGS: 59 (top)

Licences

'Water features' and 'Tourist information' on page 16 is based upon Crown Copyright and is reproduced with the permission of Land & Property Services under delegated authority from the Controller of Her Majesty's Stationery Office, Crown copyright and database right 2015 PMLPA No 100496

'Basic map skills' on page 15 was adapted from © CCEA 2022: Reproduced with permission of the Northern Ireland Council for the Curriculum, Examinations and Assessment.